Illness, Work,
and Poverty

ILLNESS, WORK,

William T. Query

and POVERTY

The Hospital/Factory
in Rehabilitation

Jossey-Bass Inc., Publishers
615 Montgomery Street · San Francisco · 1968

THE JOSSEY-BASS
BEHAVIORAL SCIENCE SERIES

General Editors

WILLIAM E. HENRY, *University of Chicago*
NEVITT SANFORD, *Stanford University and Wright Institute, Berkeley*

To
Jonathan and Evan

Preface

This book is an outgrowth of my research while I served as senior psychologist in a rehabilitation hospital in England during 1964 and 1965. It soon became apparent to me that the wealth of material to be obtained from this unusual setting would be of interest to many who, like myself, believe that methods used in mental hospitals have implications in other areas. The purpose of this book is to share a theoretical approach that has meaning not only for hospital programs but for programs, such as the Job Corps, whose staff personnel are committed to the rehabilitation of persons to the "world of work." The book will obviously be a guide to these people and have the most meaning for them. As a description of an institutional plan, it presents material in which psychologists, social workers, nurses, psychiatrists, sociologists, and hospital administrators will find something of relevance to their own profession. I have permitted myself to express some biased remarks in analyzing the direction I think my own profession and others should take to benefit society at large.

The scope of the book is broadened in the final chapters, where discussion is given over to the application of the method to other social problems. These problems—poverty and the loss of purpose in life—concern everyone who reads his morning newspaper, as well as those who cannot afford one to read. The book will serve a vital need for social and behavioral scientists interested in this problem, and especially for those interested in how social problems can be investigated from the viewpoint of personality research.

The plan of the book is somewhat unprecedented in that, while the major conclusions are presented in Chapters 5 and 6, the step-by-step investigations, upon which these conclusions are based, are presented in monograph form in Appendices A through G. All materials pertaining to the rationale, subjects, method of the studies, and statistical data are included in separate appendices. Discussion not vital to my main concern—that is, application of the treatment program to other areas—is included in these extended appendices. This arrangement is for the convenience of the reader, so that he may relate the major results of the evaluation of the hospital/factory to important extensions of the plan without being interrupted by supplementary details.

Chapters 1 and 2 are devoted to the purposes of this book and my thoughts about poverty. Chapters 3 and 4 introduce the reader to the uniqueness of the institution. The remaining chapters deal with my evaluation of it, one of its salient programs, and a theoretical approach that may, if properly instituted, deal meaningfully with specific social programs in a "new" environment.

The promise of a new environment such as the rehabilitation hospital (hospital/factory) cannot be realized without people like the hospital's physician superintendent, Dr. Roger Morgan, who centers so prominently in this book. He kindly shared his thoughts on community psychiatry with me. His understanding of the problems of research was necessary for the writing of this book and his editorial comments were invaluable. I am indebted to Graham Till, now at Powick Hospital (England), for his assistance in the actual collection of the research material, and also to my friends and colleagues on the staff who served both as subjects and raters. To the many patients who were so cooperative, and indeed interested in being subjects, I again wish a satisfying life after their discharge.

While the opinions stated in this book in no way reflect those of the Veterans Administration, I wish to express my gratitude to the V.A. and particularly to Dr. A. Dudley Roberts, chief of psychology service; Dr. Kenneth B. Moore, director of research; and

Dr. Aaron Mason, director, all of the V.A. Hospital, Lexington, Kentucky, for granting me the leave to undertake this assignment. I want especially to thank Dr. Joseph Lyons,[1] research psychologist of the same hospital, Professor Jerome L. Singer, director of clinical psychology training, City College of the City University of New York, and Professor William E. Henry, Committee on Human Development, University of Chicago, for reading portions of the manuscript or the manuscript in its entirety and their advice on the planning of this book. I am indebted to the staff of the North Dakota State University Computing Center for checking the accuracy of the data analyses. I want to commend Miss Renee Setness, Mrs. Lila Lovgren, Miss Judi Linder, Miss Janet Steckler, and Miss Dilys Jones for their typing skill in working on various phases of the manuscript. Finally, I am deeply grateful to my wife, Dr. Joy M. Query, for her long effort in the difficult job of editing the manuscript. She made many valuable suggestions out of her own contact with the rehabilitation hospital. We found rehabilitation a rewarding experience in "England's green and pleasant land."

Fargo, North Dakota   WILLIAM T. QUERY
August 1968

---

[1] Now at the University of California, Davis.

Contents

Illness, Work, and Poverty

 *ONE*

Orientation and Objectives

The primary focus of this book is on the debilitating effects of poverty on the people who are poor, and the alleviation of these effects. The method proposed is extrapolated from the rehabilitative treatment of the mentally ill. This method has been developed in Great Britain to aid in the rehabilitation of the chroni-

cally incapacitated and unemployed who are mentally disturbed.

It is natural that there should be a cross-fertilization between mental illness and poverty as areas of public concern. New courses have been charted in the institutional treatment of the mentally ill, and in recent decades new ideas about caring for the poor have been encouraged. Programs and aspirations of planners in one area have often suggested changes in the other; a converging of these streams of social concern is, therefore, inevitable. This book deals with a theory and method by which this convergence can be realized.

What happens to an institution when the inmates' problems are conceived to be economic as well as social, psychological, and psychiatric? What changes are brought about in the people who work with them? These questions require in our thinking a transition from mental illness to poverty and a new perspective on institutional life as a whole. This book analyzes this transition and its broad meaning in a variety of areas within the field of human welfare. We consider poverty in two guises—material poverty and the

1

poverty of incentive—both of which feed on each other and are detrimental to this welfare.

We studied virtually an entire hospital staff and its patients, who were also workers in the factory there, in order to find answers to these questions. We systematically used the techniques of clinical and social psychology, which we specially selected in order to make meaningful generalizations to a normal but poor population.

Generalizing is always a problem in a theoretical book. Extrapolating from the work being carried on with mentally disturbed people and relating it to the impoverished has its special hazards. One approach is to encourage productivity as a way of meeting psychological needs and motives, regardless of the health of the individual.

Occasionally I will find it necessary to cite studies on social roles using schizophrenic individuals as subjects. This is inevitable in the study of the work people perform in mental institutions where these people predominate and where their particular psychopathology largely determines the degree of competence they display in the institutions. Data from schizophrenics will likewise be used in the evaluation of the approach in this book.

Schizophrenics, perhaps more than other mentally disturbed people, serve to highlight the problems faced by the impoverished. An important component in their difficulties is social isolation. The poor, jobless, and homeless men, with whom we deal in a later chapter, are also often socially isolated and inadequate. There is a loss of sustained activity in both groups, particularly among itinerant men. The debilitating nature of poverty produces in many of the poor the craving for dependency that characterizes schizophrenics. Finally, individual members of both groups are often underachievers. As a result, members of both groups are frequently urged by their families, neighbors, and society to do something for themselves. Admittedly, the poverty-ridden person does not share the primary and secondary symptoms of mental disorders. Nevertheless, the schizophrenic person and other disturbed people share with the poverty victim, to a remarkable extent, the residual effects and the social and motivational inadequacies that constitute the psychology of poverty.

The data in this book are derived from mentally disturbed people who live in England and not from any in the United States. National differences will be discussed wherever appropriate. From my rehabilitative practice in both the United States and Great Britain, I have observed that these differences may lie chiefly in the deference and respect for authority, but these differences can be easily overestimated.

The objectives of this book are best stated as follows:

1. As stated earlier, our first objective is to propose a systematic theory of rehabilitation in terms of the social interaction surrounding work. The key concepts in this framework are work role, work orientation, role model, reference group, and self-image. (The following definitions of these concepts will be illustrated by the practice of apprenticeship, which is still common in the field of hairdressing.) *Work role* is the total coordinated behavior expected by others who view the performer as a working member of the society. The student coming to the shop before the owner, arranging the chairs, and unlocking the drawers are examples of the apprentice work role. *Work orientation* is the role model's attitude toward the work role. Does he view his early arrival as important to running the shop? Does he believe that work promotes mental and physical health, or is it, and especially his apprenticeship, merely a necessary step toward future rewards? *Role model* is the person to whom the apprentice has been formally or informally assigned and for whom he may have specific feelings as related to his chosen field of work. The role model is one or more persons considered in a special category because of their expertise in a particular type of work, as is the head barber for the apprentice, or, in the hospital/factory, as is the nurse for the patient in the social area of work in general. *Reference group* is that group to which the person with whom the role model interacts refers as an affiliated member. The person, for example, who is chronically on relief may refer to himself as a member of that segment of the population which is hopelessly poor. He may even deny that he is a member of the labor force at all. For the apprentice, the reference group is the group of trainees, or only the trainees in his particular class. He may derive satisfaction from considering himself similar to a popular actor who portrays a medical

intern. The relationship of teacher to pupil is similar; both trainee and pupil are apprentices of a kind. The reference group in this instance is the same. *Self-image* is based on the complex of descriptive traits that the person who is interacting with the role model ascribes to himself. *Unemployable* may be such a self-image shared by both the hospitalized mental patient and the poverty victim. These images are subject to change in the interacting, or modeling, process.[1] The apprentice may perceive himself as *semi-employed*. If he fails consistently in unlocking the drawers and is admonished for his neglect he may form the self-image of *careless*.

2. Our second objective is to describe a particular type of institution in actual operation and to show how it holds promise for the changes we believe are socially important. Its institutional structure is consistent with our theory of socially derived self-images. Various modifications within the structure of the hospital/factory are proposed to meet the unique problems intrinsic to the psychology of poverty.

3. Our third objective is to show how the structure of such an institution, which we shall call a "hospital/factory," can be both hospital and factory at the same time, with both the benefits and the hazards derived from this combination. The term "factory" is used for want of a better term. Such an institution, called also a "rehabilitation hospital," offers to the person undergoing rehabilitation not only factory work but many other types of labor as well.

4. Our fourth objective, beyond showing the occupational aspect of the hospital/factory, is to show how social competence is restored by an educational scheme that is integrated into the work and organizational structure of the institution. This is a training program in savings, budgeting, and other areas indirectly connected with work. We cannot call this educational scheme "work," but for the culturally deprived this sphere of rehabilitation has its importance in his learning the judicious use of the tangible rewards from work and the satisfaction that comes from understanding his environment. Fear and confusion often accompany the restoration of a person who has lost contact with or is overwhelmed by such a spe-

---

[1] This process should not be confused with the evaluation process of the hospital/factory in a subsequent chapter.

cialized society as ours. The educational procedures described here
allay much of this fear in a highly practical and meaningful manner.

5. The last objective is to show how assessment procedures
built into a hospital/factory operate on two levels of evaluation:
(1) It is possible to assess the attitudes of staff both toward their
work in the hospital and toward the patients with whom they are
working because every staff member has some type of work relationship with the patients. It is also possible to determine the attitudes of the patients who achieve in such a setting. These assessments can be introduced into the hospital structure at will but are
not routinely used. (2) There are the systematic and recurrent assessments of the patients themselves as a part of the work role of
the staff. Both levels of evaluation are important regardless of the
population to be served by the hospital/factory, for only through
such evaluations can we have empirical bases for our broad generalizations to the poverty victim.

The definition of work involved in Chapters 3 and 4 will
be confined, when the hospital is described and analyzed, to factory-
type production, domestic chores, and clerical and farming activities. Work in broader terms and as a meaningful activity will be
analyzed in other chapters. In each instance, our definition will denote an activity that requires effort and for which one receives recognition and reward. We will therefore analyze briefly the psychology of effort and reward. More pertinent to the study will be the
social aspects of work activity. These aspects are highlighted in the
rehabilitative institution described in Chapter 3 and in our theoretical approach discussed in the next chapter.

TWO

The Nature of Poverty

When we speak of poverty, we mean something more than material poverty and drain on the economy. The poverty that we have in mind is as damaging to the civilization as it is to the economy. Among those of us who partake of America's affluence, it is the poverty of empathy between individuals that makes us shut away from our feeling the growing number of people of all ages who are unable to sustain themselves. Among the poor, or near-poor, it is the poverty of self-confidence and the image of themselves that slowly results from working below their capacity or not working at all. These people we will call the "poverty victims."[1] The method described in Chapter 3 could potentially relieve both material and mental poverty.

The poverty from which many of us suffer has, therefore, its social psychological implications and requires a social psychological solution. We will describe briefly the problem, its causes, and its effects as found in the literature.

Americans have indeed achieved a uniqueness among modern societies; Max Lerner calls the society the "American civilization" (Lerner, 1957). Our problems may or may not be unique. They may be so much a part of us that diagnosing them may be difficult. We cannot ignore the fact that a certain down-

[1] We might readily call the rest of us the "affluence victims," because we contend that our affluence and especially the technology that has brought it about have victimized us.

6

grading of interpersonal relationships, despite our intense study of them (of how we think of others and how we think of ourselves), has been etched into the American society. Parallel with this downgrading has been a technological advance the rapidity of which is astounding. The first process has been gradual; the second, quite the opposite. The two processes have combined to leave our cities and towns populated with a backwash of unwanted, disadvantaged individuals who have only now become recognized as national burdens. I shall describe one plan, based on social psychological principles, that can be adapted to reclaim many of these people.

Methods of dealing with the problems of loss of self-esteem and joblessness have usually focused on side effects—vagrancy, sickness, riots, crime—but not upon the causes. Law enforcement officers have dealt with some of these individuals, but the mass of Americans have met the problems with indifference, or suggested solutions like a guaranteed income or an occasional contribution to a charity. People who either neglect the problems or turn to methods like legislation or financial aid show little realization of the nature of the problems in their psychological terms.

When we view the problem psychologically, it is patently evident that the rehabilitation of poverty victims, like that of any other group of handicapped people, will have to be accomplished by a painstaking, individual approach. Only in this way can latent feelings of self-worth be bolstered and old skills retrained.

Overspecialization, where one person is required to know only a segment of a product, a firm, or only those working closest to him, has been cited as one of the primary causes of the increase of the unemployable and the schism between modern man and his neighbor (Goodman, 1965). Technology, which has made the art of fabrication and the pride of the guild obsolete, has been suggested as a cause of the loss of involvement with one's work. Even the service jobs have lost considerable prestige and commitment on the part of those who perform them.

Beyond the growing number of jobless and the loss of empathic understanding, the tendency of people to communicate only with their "kind," only with, for example, people of the same educational level, or only with people from the same specialization within a profession, has been brought about by overspecialization. There have been rising demands for social services and an increasing need for family therapy. These trends may indicate that the schism of interpersonal relationships and loss of respect for others have invaded even the closely knit life that has always characterized Western (and American) family relationships.

Through several revisions, Jules Henry, in his book *Culture Against Man* (1963), has described the increase of "human obsolescence" as a culturally derived phenomenon. He isolated as the cause our propensity to be driven by and to value competitiveness and expansiveness as though they were physiological drives. He studied three institutions for the aged (two public and one private) that were representative of the places that care for people who became obsolete at the end of their productive life. Disengagement among the residents and between the residents and the staff characterized to some degree all of these institutions.

When obsolescence occurs as unemployment at the peak of a man's productivity, its effects on the person can be variously categorized. Zawadzki and Lazarsfeld (1935) found in an early study that the common reactions were (1) apathy, (2) distress, (3) resignation, or (4) being unbroken by the catastrophe.

In the mass unemployment during the Great Depression, many who lost their jobs did not wish to be identified with those depending upon relief. A different situation prevails today. There is a more insidious increase in unemployment and in the number of persons who are commonly thought to be "unemployable." Dependency, both psychological and material, characterizes many of these people.

Margaret Wood, in her book *Paths of Loneliness: The Individual Isolated in Modern Society* (1953), suggests that dependency is the chief difference between the unemployed and the unemployable. The unemployable tend, more than the unemployed, to feel dependent upon such programs as the Works Progress Administration, which the public regarded to a great extent as created work. She offers as a solution the unification of interpersonal relationships, but points out that the person who is the "loner" in society is obliged to make an effort on his own behalf to be rehabilitated.

It is the premise of this book that the loners, the poverty victims, cannot make such an effort themselves, because they *are* loners. These are the same elderly, psychogenically impaired individuals whom Lowenthal and Berkman (1967) described in their "social invisibility" hypothesis. This asocial "protective coloration" keeps these people out of institutions that could, if properly designed, help them. A concerted program must be created to seek them out, and rehabilitation must incorporate principles to enhance interpersonal relationships. By adopting such an approach, the rest of us can be helped in re-establishing our kinship with others on a healthier plane.

We must reiterate that we do not equate the impoverished person with the mentally ill person except in the special sense of impoverishment of self-esteem. This impoverishment can take place either within or outside of an institution. As we have seen, the persons caught by the social effects of poverty, particularly those who have been receiving only marginal welfare sustenance for years, show many of the characteristics, such as apathy and dependency, of persons who have been institutionalized for a long period of time. It is for this reason that we discuss at length the effects of work on the life of the persons in institutions.

In the following chapters we will describe the positive effects that were brought about by institutional rehabilitation in the form of the rehabilitation hospital. The phrase "institutional rehabilitation" suggests bringing about a change in the environment of an institution as a basis for bringing about a change in those who live there. We submit that such a change can be made and is important in rehabilitating many institutional cases. Individual change is hastened, we believe, by increasing the social interaction and the demands for responsibility, without increasing the complexities of the environment. The "rehabilitated institution" also meets the individual's loss of social involvement by permitting him to change in order to meet social requirements.

Much of the alleviation of the subtle effects of poverty and unemployment will come through specially planned institutions set up to re-educate and revitalize the impoverished and unwanted. In order for us to understand how the effects of prolonged poverty can be changed through such a plan of rehabilitation, we must be familiar with the change that has been witnessed in institutions. We will concentrate on institutions for the mentally ill because it is in these institutions that much of the relevant research on institutional change has been done.

We will discuss the impact on mental hospitals of the recent emphasis on community psychiatry and work programs. This emphasis has gained momentum in the last decade. It is customary to set the date of the beginning of this movement with Dr. George Bell's opening of Dingleton Hospital in Melrose, Scotland, in 1947; this event is important as a beginning of the changes that have since occurred. The lack of restraint of the "open" hospital is basic to any program of change, whether it is applied to the unemployable or to chronically ill mental patients.

We will discuss how the patient perceives himself in the institution and how these perceptions can be measured according to our theoretical framework.

Such concepts as the reference group and self-image can very well apply to the poverty victim. The study of the staff workers and their orientation toward their work in the hospital and their change in role can apply to those whose job it is to help the poverty victim.

New environments evolve as any other social phenomenon does, and they are new only in the sense that they incorporate, sometimes in a different way, the characteristics of other environments. The institutional environment of the chronic mental patient has evolved from the mental hospitals of Pinel's day. The community environment of the poverty victim has evolved similarly from the debtors' prisons described by Charles Dickens. These evolutions come about by investigations and legislative reform, and by changes in attitudes of society toward the care of these people. Environments consistent with the prevailing attitudes are then created and assimilated into the social structure.

Poverty is a process, just as institutionalization is a process. There is no subculture of poverty victims; nor is there one of people in mental hospitals. They share only the demoralization brought on by the demeaning aspect of their loss of productivity.

Man has been confronted with the waste of human resources from illness or other incapacities for centuries, and he has coped with individuals he could not understand in many and varied ways. At times he has venerated these persons; at other times he has condemned them. The mentally ill person, for example, has been received in one society as an agent of a deity; in another, he has been tortured as a demon, or restrained in chains with only his inner voices for companionship. Only very recently has he been retrained, and more rarely, employed. The poverty victim gave himself over to the Crusades and war or found some ascribed status in a rigid class system.

We believe that our understanding of both mental illness and poverty is enhanced by our assisting both the mentally ill and the sane but poor person toward greater understanding of themselves in a community-like situation within the institution. Because of this belief, retraining the mentally ill person has been elevated to the status of a treatment procedure. The social distance between the "keeper" and the "kept" has been reduced to a remarkable extent. Whether this closeness promotes insight into the phenomenal experience of being mentally ill or changes public opinion toward the patient is irrelevant to many of those who work daily with patients. They view the patient as a mixture of assets and liabilities, as a person with certain annoying symptoms that interfere with constructive work habits, and, if he has been hospitalized, a person very much a victim of the regimentation characteristic of some mental hospitals.

The effects of institutionalization, rather than of illness as such, tend to dominate the thinking of those working in hospitals like St. Wulstan's, the hospital described in this book. Their primary interest is in rehabilitation, and they focus their attention on the effects of prior treatment rather than on the cure or etiology of an endogenous affliction. Institutionalization is conceived to be an endemic "disease," and the patients are called "institutionalized" persons. Some speak of institutionalization in matters of degree, but rarely of kind, and certain behaviors come to be expected of the fully institutionalized person. Inertness, passivity, occasional acts of hostility, and a loss of aptitude are their dominant attributes. The institutionalized person is a person who has forgotten how to learn, and knows not what he needs to know.

It is not surprising that yet another institution, that is, the rehabilitation hospital, or hospital/factory, has been set up specifically to counteract these effects and to determine with what type of person and to what extent change is possible.

It is reasonable that such an institution of reclamation will help some patients, and, although without empirical evidence, we believe that a similar approach can help the poverty victim, as well as the mental patient, to form a new image of himself. The professional role of the staff member will also alter. We will focus upon the staff in the anticipation that the general approach will be used in these other areas, such as retraining the unskilled and unemployed worker who is counted among the poor.

We will frequently refer in this book to psychiatric hospitals and hospitals in general, and to rehabilitation hospitals in particular. In some sense, every hospital has its rehabilitative aspects in the degree to which its function and facilities are committed by the staff to rehabilitation. The term "rehabilitation hospital" is reserved to apply to all those facilities that, in their entirety, are built or renovated for the purpose of industrial rehabilitation. Rehabilitation hospitals can be for psychiatric or physical cases, or both. The hospital/factory described in Chapter 3 happens to be exclusively for psychiatric patients.

◄§ HOSPITAL PROJECTS §►

Hospital industries are an acceptable part of the mental hospital organization and many such programs exist. Staffs of some hospitals pride themselves on a 20 per cent working patient population. Special programs exist for geriatric patients (Mason *et al.*, 1963; Mason, 1965). The patients in these programs do much of the menial work where the patient can remain seated, such as folding hospital socks. As an extension of this movement toward the expansion of hospital industry, contracts have been secured for patients housed in halfway houses and hostels. This has been found valuable for maintaining the patients' interest in a vocation when they cannot return to the hospital each day for their work.

The hospital/factory is one project among many that have been launched with this growing interest in work for the patient. There are specific characteristics of an environmental nature that distinguish this type of rehabilitation hospital from these other projects and are the reason for its unique promise. In their book, *Psychiatric Rehabilitation: Some Problems of Research,* Kandel and Williams (1964) critically analyze several projects from the standpoint of operational, administrative, and methodological problems and attempted solutions. Many of these problems are intrinsic to the hospital/factory; the problems may be more complex than the traditional mental hospital, because innovations that have characterized mental hospitals for the past thirty years are combined in the structure of the hospital/factory. These innovations are: (1) the "openness" of the hospital, (2) the change of the staff's attitude, brought about by such responsibilities as serving as role models for patients, (3) a program of social re-education for a select group of patients who require this training, and (4) the democratic nature of the therapeutic community woven into interstaff relationships as well as relationships between patient and staff and between patient and patient. The hospital/factory adds to this characteristic the monetary incentive of the hospital program as a commercial enterprise. This last feature best identifies it as a new and fruitful approach for application to populations other than the mentally ill.

Rehabilitation in hospitals is in its infancy, and many changes that this movement may generate can only be surmised from the preliminary data that we have at hand. One effect can be anticipated with certainty if programs such as these are adopted on a large scale: there will be a problem of re-evaluating the statistical category in which the institutional person is placed. We shall use one source to illustrate the problem.

Wolfbein (1964), for example, does not include in his calculations of the labor force the inmates of institutions or children under fourteen years of age. Using the "activity" concept, he classifies the labor force into active and inactive employed, and active

and inactive unemployed. All inmates are automatically placed outside the scheme and those who are retired but not institutionalized
are counted, but outside the labor force. There are three relevant
points: (1) A patient in the hospital/factory might legitimately be
classified as "active unemployed" as far as the hospital is concerned,
but he should be reclassified as either active or inactive. Most of the
patients in such a program would not consider themselves retired
from work. Even if they were retired, they would appear in the labor
computation, but they are not included at all in Wolfbein's scheme.
(2) Patients should be classified in terms of the community, that is,
they should be classified as "active unemployed" in the full knowledge that the ultimate goal is community employment. This procedure would swell only slightly the numbers in this category, and
would not create a false picture, if our ideas of rehabilitation are
sound. (3) In the hospital/factory the working staff are classified,
according to these recommendations, "active employed"; however,
in most cases, the patients are doing the same tasks as staff members but are placed in a different category. Is this classification reasonable? We must hold to one point of reference—the community.
Although introducing productive and paid work into the hospital
creates problems of classification for those interested in labor statistics, it is well to remember that the hospital is not an employing
firm in the full sense of the term. It is not a community employer,
and as such it does not hire or terminate employment. It is, however, dependent upon seasonal changes, migration, and other factors
that affect businesses in general. As we shall see, it also has peculiar
problems of its own, such as overlapping contracts and the effect of
having several mentally ill people in all stages of recovery working
together.

⊷§ EFFECTS OF ENVIRONMENT §⊷

In the term "institutionalized" person, we include for the
purpose of this book the professional and lay members of the institution staff as well as the patients. The environment of the hospital
affects the attitudes and work performance of the staff members in
predictable ways. This has been discovered not only in this project

but in the projects that radically altered the organization of specific wards (Fairweather, 1964; Colarelli and Siegel, 1966). We assume that the effect of institutional life without work is similar to the effect of chronic unemployment and deprivation on the self-image of many of those erstwhile mentally healthy persons outside the institution.

The theory that the social environment is related to the manifestations of the illness has been investigated (Roberts and Myers, 1959). It might be more succinct to state that environmental stress situations, such as poverty, affect health through the mediation of one's perception of the situation, as has been shown by Hinkle and Wolff (1957). We concur that perception of the environment is important for understanding reactions to it.

The corollary that the extent of recovery from stress depends on the procedures utilizing the social environment of the person is being analyzed by social scientists (Brown, 1961; Goffman, 1962; Jones, 1953; Belknap, 1956; Stanton and Schwartz, 1954; Rapoport, 1960; Levinson and Gallagher, 1964). Rapoport and his associates, for example, have shown in their study of Henderson Hospital how stresses accrue when the special ideological milieu of permissiveness in the hospital is followed by the more demanding milieu of the outside community. Manasse (1965) has shown that this change of milieu affects the self-image of the patients. As this investigator suggests, the patients' high self-regard in the protected hospital environment is attributable to the minimum demands made upon them. When they feel more demands, their self-regard is lowered—or raised, on occasion, to a more realistic level.

Self-regard is one possible explanatory concept determining the extent of recovery, but psychological theory has not generally entered into descriptions of hospital programs, except in the more recent studies of attitude therapy (Treatment Team, 1965) and the hospital environment by Cumming and Cumming (1962) and Edelson (1965) within the framework of ego psychology. Cumming and Cumming related work to ego integrity and cited the Netherne Hospital in England as an example of an institutional environment that promotes recovery from ego disorganization. Edelson integrated group and individual therapy into the therapeutic setting of the hospital milieu. None of these authors has extended hospital treatment one step further into the area of the rehabilitation of the poor, which is the main objective of this book.

The hospital environment has been related to the general humanistic ideology of patient care, and this in turn to the personality characteristics and sociotherapeutic orientation of the staff (Gilbert and Levinson, 1957; Sharaf and Levinson, 1957). Few of these studies, or others in the field, have dealt as we have with the special circumstances created in the institution when the workshop and social re-education of the patients are given primary emphasis. This latter type of environment is seen in its purest form in the hospital/factory.[2]

Actually, a compromise is being sought between the permissive ideology of a hospital like Henderson, where interaction is encouraged, and the more directive ideology of the rehabilitation hospital, where completely free interaction is not permitted to interfere with the productivity of the patients. These compromises are found in the meetings themselves, for example, in the program at Henderson. Where both the ideology of work and the ideology of free interaction exist, staff misunderstanding can develop. Sometimes the hospital policy is more permissive and the ideas of an efficient workshop are contrary to the implementation of the policy. This situation has been described by Landy and Raulet (1959) in the study of the work supervisor's role.

Staff meetings are, therefore, necessary to clarify the hospital ideology in any type of psychiatric hospital (and, presumably, for any program designed to rehabilitate the unemployable). It frequently develops that the doctor approaches the meeting from the framework of the permissive ideology and the other members of the staff approach the meeting from the directive framework of the work-

---

[2] Out of practical necessity, the industrial workshop is being introduced wherever feasible, as Kandel and Williams report (1964). In contrast with the projects these investigators surveyed and those Edelson and the Cummings analyzed, less emphasis is placed in the rehabilitation hospital or hospital/factory on interpersonal or group dynamics and greater emphasis on the output of the patient. Although this seems to be a growing trend, it is safe to report that most hospital industries still form only a small part of the larger institution where dynamics are emphasized.

shop, or wherever they may be working. Misunderstandings arise about the purpose of the meetings themselves. An inability to resolve differences in viewpoint can be indirectly detrimental to the life of the institutionalized person.

To understand the stress that a change in ideology may place on the staff member as an "institutional person," we must understand the nature of the change from a total institution to a less than total institution. We will first consider the total institution.

THE TOTAL INSTITUTION

The total institution (Goffman, 1962) is a heuristic concept for explaining many phenomena witnessed in the behavior of patients who have undergone hospitalization. Although Goffman includes therapeutic communities in his category, the idea that a self-contained unit, such as a total institution, can be established as a special hospital to rehabilitate long-term patients from other total institutions is a new one. Establishing such a place for the chronic mental patient is what we mean by "rehabilitating institutions." The rationale for such an innovation is the growing conviction that only through a prepared environment, where the productivity of the patient is increased and where total responsibility for the conduct of his life is placed on the patient, can chronicity be reversed.

Interest in hospital projects (Kandel and Williams, 1964) has been increased by the realization that the mental hospital is an example of an aberrant social system (which Goffman called the "total institution") (Goffman, 1962). Lethargy and loss of individuality of the patient due to the social isolation of such an environment have been described both in autobiographical novels and in scientific treatises (Sommer and Osmond, 1965).

The symptoms these patients show have been called an "institutional neurosis" (Barton, 1959). This neurotic reaction is a clinical syndrome largely dependent upon hospitalization; it is independent of the basic disturbance and deviancy that brought about the patient's admission. If environmental theory is meaningful, such a reaction can be reversed by changing the characteristics of the environment that contributed to the reaction.

To free hospitals of those characteristics that institutionalize the person—such as the dualism between the world of the staff and the world of the patient and the restriction of social involvement— the staffs of many of the projects described by Kandel and Williams (1964), and especially the staff of the rehabilitation hospital to be described in Chapter 3, have evolved a system of minimizing the distance between these worlds and maximizing social involvement of both patient and staff. Hospital authorities still recognize the need for patients and staff members to identify with their worlds. This need is partially fulfilled by such patient organizations as patient government, and, in the rehabilitation hospital, it is in part the function of the Patients' Sports and Social Club. There are often directly analogous organizations for staff members. Total social involvement is also not emphasized in many projects for the same reason, and attendance at group meetings and membership in the organizations are frequently voluntary.

Another way of breaking down the totality of the mental hospital is placing patients in community working situations. These placements have been important parts of the program in many rehabilitation projects. Further progress in bringing the community into the institution is achieved by recurrent reports, from employers, of patient behavior. This procedure, which is discussed in Chapter 3, gives employers the feeling that the staff of the institution is interested in the placement and in the employer himself, without creating the aura of interference that a personal visit from a member of the staff might create. This does not mean that a personal visit in time of stress is not highly important; it is, particularly shortly after placement.

Change in the mental hospital has been followed by change in professional roles. Community placements are often the duty of the social worker in mental hospitals as well as of the social worker who works in poverty areas where jobs must be found. Sometimes specific social workers have responsibilities for one type of placement exclusively. With the emphasis on rehabilitation, the pressure of placement often leaves little time for casework, for which the social worker has been trained. The role of the social worker, therefore, also changes with the changing conditions.

Community placement does not affect the nurse in the hospital/factory directly, but any new ideology poses problems for the nurse in other ways. The nursing role is often ambiguous at best and the nurse has little or no professional self-identity. This situation prevails in both general and psychiatric hospitals (Corwin and Taves, 1963), and would also apply to the nurse whose interest lay in poverty programs.

In the sociological literature on the nursing profession, it has been found useful to use the term "role." In this context, the training role is called the "role model." This use is similar, but not identical, to our use of the term in the theory discussed in Chapter 7. The actual role, termed the "role performance," is the role the staff member assumes when hired (Schwartz, 1957).[3] The hospital/factory ideology poses problems for nurses trained outside the rehabilitation hospital and in the traditional psychiatric hospital or nursing school. The role model (to use Schwartz's definition) is at variance with the role performance. The conflict between roles that are traditional role models and those that are "ascribed," or performed, is found most vividly in the nurses' expectations of their duties in the workshop. Oftentimes the nurse is ill-prepared for the duties he is expected to perform in the workshop or in the patient meetings.

It is generally true that the training of nurses and the ideology of nursing roles are different among different countries, as shown by Altschul (1963). In many countries, such as Britain and the United States, the specific training of the nurse fails to include the body of knowledge required for the nursing role in the area of rehabilitation. Following a review of the role of the patient, we will return to the discussion of the staff as it is transformed by rehabilitation.

Still another use of the term "role" is found in Parsons' study of the sick person (Parsons, 1958). The psychiatric rehabilitation hospital has its greatest impact on the role of the person as a sick member of society. The sick role entails certain standards of behav-

---

[3] In Schwartz's analysis, the role model was prescribed by the hospital administrator and not, as used here, by the instructors at the training hospital. This is a critical distinction, as the function of both instructors and the administrator in this context are the same.

ior and obligations that permit exemptions from traditional social responsibilities. The person emphasizes the sick role most at the time he seeks admission to a hospital for treatment. The sick role (and, we may assume, the "poverty victim role") can exempt the person to such an extent that the "secondary gains" accrued from the situation make it difficult for the patient to fulfill the obligation of helping himself to recover. Others are expected to allow the sick person enough time for recovery. The amount of time allowed depends on the type and seriousness of illness, the financial and familial stress under which the sick person is laboring at the time, his age, and, to some extent, his sex. If he is a man and wage-earner, expectations are greater and more time is required.

Psychiatric illness (and prolonged poverty) is generally considered to be of long duration; therefore the suffering person is exempted from responsibilities and, barring early and effective treatment, the sick role is prolonged for several years through various phases of relapse and remission. In some instances, social responsibilities, such as driving a car or being considered competent to sign checks, are considered beyond the capacities of the psychotic. There is no analogous situation for the poverty victim, who is expected to enjoy the fruits of affluence.[4]

The sick role relieves the person of the responsibility of working to support his family. There is a focus upon the self as a disabled worker, and the family is viewed as one that has a disabled member. The concept of a disturbed family implies disturbed family relationships, and this disturbance is often lessened by the hospitalization of one of the members. Similarly, families may be relieved of the social responsibility toward the ill person by the intervention of the hospital, which takes temporary control of the person's behavior. Relinquishing this responsibility may not be easy and the guilt family members feel is sometimes acute.

By placing the person in a work situation as treatment, psy-

[4] The current trend in surgical and other medical practices is for the doctor to encourage early recovery by advising against lengthy recuperation and intervening more directly in the process of recovery. Psychiatrists are similarly inclined, and the emphasis on work programs for the mentally ill is a manifestation of this trend.

chiatric hospital authorities may heighten any guilt the family members feel. The gulf between what the family expects of the patient in his sick role and what the hospital seems to expect from him is widened, and misunderstanding on the part of the family members is the result. Hospitals are expected to conform to commonly held expectations in relieving patients from responsibilities, just as families with ailing members are expected to hospitalize them. When these expectations are not fulfilled, as in a deliberate program of "working the patient," the relationship between family, patient, and hospital is not in balance. The family anticipates that the hospital will protect the patient from those things the family expects him incapable of doing. The patient expects not to be called upon to do things contrary to his expectations in the sick role. The hospital expects the family to be more willing and interested in reaccommodating a patient shown to be capable of performing those tasks of which he has been relieved.

A hospital where the chief treatment is work, in comparison with hospitals where there is a lack of work, is more conspicuous for not fulfilling its role of protecting the patient from imposed responsibility. The way a person in the surrounding community views this type of hospital is interesting, particularly when this person does not have a member of his family hospitalized. He may not share the sick role expectations as we have outlined them, and he may see the rehabilitation hospital as a needed facility for relieving the taxpayer of the financial burden of supporting hospitals. If he is a strongly involved member of a trade union, he may sense some threat to his standing and set the working patient apart from the labor force— "They really do not work out there as we do here in the firm." If he is a manager, he may be interested in the quality and quantity of the products made and how they affect his own interests. He may even, under given employment conditions, consider the rehabilitation hospital an added source of labor, where the capabilities and mental status of the employees are known by professional people, that is, psychiatrists.

For the patient, work in the hospital has the effect of confusing the boundaries of competence. Mental competence is usually interpreted by the patient and family to blanket all social responsibilities, but in hospital practice may cover only a few. The lack of responsibility on the part of the patient has special legal implications and sanctions if certain acts are performed. The boundaries are usually more stringently drawn in a court of law, where competence is pronounced by jurors, than in a hospital, where means of achieving more and greater responsibility through treatment are practiced. In the hospital, for example, the more fluid boundaries encompass all sorts of work activity, but not supervised recreation. These boundaries may cover the freedom of spending the reward for work, but not work itself.

The staff of the rehabilitation hospital does not fail to consider competence, but the approach is different. The rehabilitation hospital philosophy assumes that all patients are socially competent until proven otherwise by their behavior. (Similarly, those who are unemployed only because of increasing specialization are held to be competent to handle the complexities of modern society.)

This appears at first glance to be a lack of caution that is contradictory to societal expectations for the mentally ill person. Incompetence, as displayed by the patient in the rehabilitation hospital, is more quickly recognized, and the sanctions are perceptibly clearer to the patient there than they are in the community, because there is more freedom to show competent or incompetent decisions. The patient is not as emotionally involved with staff members so that the transgressions that might occur are not so quickly followed by remorse and a sense of guilt by the patient. The expectation of responsible behavior is a goal in the rehabilitation hospital; this goal is lacking in the sick role assumed by the person in other types of hospitals.

The staff member is a necessary agent in imparting feelings of competence to the hospitalized person and, likewise, to the poverty-ridden person. The relationship between the staff and the patient is not devoid of emotional involvement, but affection or hostility is subordinate to achieving a working relationship. The staff member and patient share experiences on and preferences for certain jobs, the mutual responsibility of being at the work bench on time, and the obligation of interacting in relevant terms about the myriad details of the project.

A new element is injected into the sick role and poverty role when the person is in a hospital work program that is characterized not only by greater social responsibility but greater psychomotor activity. The assumption is that the activity of work generates activity in other spheres of institution life. The assumption is partly realized in creating a physical plan that maximizes the distance between both working and recreational facilities and living quarters. The expenditure of physical effort is therefore made greater.

⋅ε§ SUMMARY ξ⋅⋅

The discussion in this chapter began with a description of how the rehabilitation of mental hospitals has proceeded from the total institution, where there were few facilities in the nature of work for the institutionalized persons to do, to another type of total institution where work is the primary *modus operandi* of the hospital. This change has not been without stress to the staffs of the hospitals in their customary roles, to the families of the patients, and to the patients themselves.

Frequent references were made to the parallel self-image between poverty victims and chronic mental patients. The poverty victim, as well as the patient, has an image of himself as being cast aside by a society of overspecialization. He feels himself dependent, however, on that society. The patient has the advantage of being able to adopt the sick role. Both suffer from a loss of self-image as a productive person.

Competence of the patient while he is in the hospital was found to be a subject of potential controversy and disagreement when work is considered as treatment. The movement in this direction, which many hospitals are taking, is thought to be "worth the candle" when the same approach is applied to the poverty victim. In a later chapter we will discuss competence in a broader theoretical perspective.

An important aspect of this movement is the breaking down of the separate worlds of the staff and patient and of the poverty victim and those who are interested in him.

We do not imply that these worlds are any more or less separated from one another in the hospital environment of the chronic mental patient or the general hospital patient, on the one hand, and the poor person and the person who is trying to help him, on the other hand. The recent emphasis placed upon the poor helping themselves suggests, in the thinking of many, that the world of the affluent and the world of the poor are intrinsically different. We will present the argument in the last chapter that, from a psychological point of view, the same needs for achievement and feelings of competence motivate both parties and what we have called a "role model" relationship is possible in a great many instances where rehabilitation is needed. In the next chapter we will describe a hospital where the needs for achievement and feelings of competence are fulfilled.

THREE

One Rehabilitation Hospital

This chapter presents a description of the hospital/factory as a prototype institution.[1] It is called a *rehabilitation hospital* here be-

[1] A briefer description of the hospital and an evaluation of its work is published in the article by R. Morgan, D. Cushing, and N. S. Manton, "A Regional Psychiatric Rehabilitation Hospital," *British Journal of Psychiatry,* 1965, 11, 955–963.

cause this name is generally given to it. However, I chose hospital/factory as a more descriptive term so as not to confuse it with those institutions designed to treat the neurologically or physically handicapped. This term also amplifies the fact that the aspects "hospital" and "factory" coexist and are essentially interchangeable. I will attempt no evaluation at this time except to give the number of patients who have been discharged, in various categories of discharges and to various living arrangements, during a specific period of time. In the following chapter, we will compare the rehabilitation hospital with similar projects. As a prototype, the hospital is, I believe, an outstanding example of the new direction rehabilitation will take. The direction will be a continuation of the general departure from custodial care with increasing patient responsibility. What is new is the emphasis on the partnership of the institution staff and patients in a venture into the world of business and industry. The hospital/factory, or rehabilitation hospital, will become a place where the role of the entrepreneur will be used as a means for achieving self-satisfaction. The way this method functions and how the identity of the hospital is retained are the focus of this chapter.

I shall describe in detail the program as it existed at the time of my evaluation. The reader will see how, had he been working in such a setting, the idea that such a program could have other uses would occur to him, and the conviction would grow. He will see in the history of the hospital/factory how the same physical plan can be adapted to a variety of rehabilitative efforts. In this example rehabilitation spanned two decades and the hospital served three types of patients: war veterans, tuberculosis patients, and mental patients. It is only a small step to serving the poor. In order to show how the program, both in its physical and communication structure, has relevance to alleviating financial and psychological poverty, I will mention as this description unfolds my thinking about the advantages it has for the poor person and particularly those without hope.

✎§ GEOGRAPHY AND PHYSICAL PLAN ξ✍

St. Wulstan's[2] Hospital is a part of the South Worcestershire Hospital Management Committee. The hospital is located in the semirural environs of the Malverns, on the lower slopes of the hills that bear this name and form the boundary between Worcestershire and Herefordshire. With a commanding view of the Malverns to the west and the Severn Valley and Bredon Hill to the east, the hospital also has the advantage of easy motor access to the community of Great Malvern and, beyond this, to the metropolitan area of greater Birmingham. This is an important feature of the hospital's location for those patients who come from the Staffordshire-Birmingham area.

The hospital itself consists of a series or rows of one-story,

---

[2] Wulstan was noted for his action in defense of his city as well as his piety in the service of the Church and State. He was born circa 1005 and made Bishop of Worcester in 1062. Although a Saxon, he assisted in the coronation of William I in 1066 and consecrated the cathedral at Worcester in 1088. He died in 1095 and was canonized in 1203.

rectangular, brick buildings, called "blocks"; these are connected by covered walkways. A narrow paved road runs through the center of the hospital grounds and divides the patients' living area (sleeping and recreational quarters, the canteen, clinic, concert hall, dining room, and television room) from the working area on the opposite side (workshops, administrative nursing offices, clerical section, social worker and chaplain offices, and factory). This physical arrangement serves to separate work from social activities; and this separation is important in our analysis of both aspects of the rehabilitation program.

Much of the work assessment, which will be discussed more fully in later chapters, goes on in the workshops themselves. Each workshop contains a large, rectangular, and open workroom, toilets, an office for the nurses, a small consulting room for the doctors, a larger meeting room with a long table for the meetings where each patient's progress is evaluated, a small kitchen where tea is prepared before the work "breaks," and a corridor lined with coathooks. A time clock and cards with the patients' names are located conspicuously at the entrance to the workshops. Behind each workshop are delivery areas. The laundry is situated at one end of the workshop area and, at the other end, kilns and other facilities for the manufacture of concrete products are located. These details are included to give the reader as complete a picture of the hospital as possible. The staff generally believe that it is ideal for their purposes and this description could serve as a guide to planners of similar programs.

A large number of staff live on the grounds in single and semi-detached dwellings near the gate. A recreation area, social club garden, hostel, the administration block, and engineering and boiler plant are located in this forward area flanking the central pavement. A small porter's lodge is located at the entrance, where inquiries may be made. This is important for first-time customers and visitors to the rehabilitation hospital. Besides dealing with inquiries, the porters have the responsibility of unobtrusively checking the neatness of the patients when they leave the grounds.

Many of the patients are able—in fact, are encouraged—to spend some time on weekends and evenings in the village public house. The "village" is Upper Welland, where good relations exist between the community outside the gate and those residing inside. A path connects the village with the hospital.

The present physical structure of St. Wulstan's, along with other hospitals in the area, was built by the British in 1939 as a receiving hospital for war casualties. The United States Army used it during the war for the same purpose. After the war it was converted into a tuberculosis sanatorium until eventually a drastic reduction of the disease in the area made this use of the facilities obsolete. For two years the hospital was unoccupied.

In 1961 a bold plan was conceived to help reduce the large, chronically ill population being treated in the psychiatric hospitals in the region. An entirely new unit solely designed for the industrial rehabilitation of a select number of these patients was to be established. This one central location was also to be made available to patients from twelve hospitals in the country areas of Worcestershire, Herefordshire, Warwickshire, Staffordshire, Shropshire, and Birmingham.[3]

An arbitrary age limit of fifty-five was set, but with no restrictions as to the duration of illness. The age of the poor is likewise a flexible factor, in that some persons older have good rehabilitative potential if they are not completely physically incapacitated.

After the initial planning, conversion and refurnishing of the blocks, and hiring of the staff was completed, the first group of patients was admitted in November 1961.

Since St. Wulstan's was planned as an experimental hospital, the first 200 admissions from the parent hospitals were matched with 116 control patients who remained in the various parent hospitals. From these 316, patients were selected for admission on a random basis. The chief consultant, physician superintendent, and other staff

[3] Since the patients come from other hospitals to the rehabilitation hospital it does not possess a "cachement area" in the true sense of the term. The hospital is also not located in the center of the area it serves but toward the southwest fringe. The hospitals from which the patients are admitted are called the parent hospitals. This casts the rehabilitation hospital in the role of junior offspring which may have been more valid after it was opened than at present. The staff is not restricted by any stringent policy from admitting promising rehabilitation prospects from hospitals outside this area.

members have made an important follow-up on the progress of these patients with careful interviews of each subject. Since the initial experiment, admission of patients has been on a selective basis, in accordance with the overall policy.

The rehabilitation hospital was not conceived to be a teaching hospital. As other industrial units have expanded and new ones have been established in Great Britain, St. Wulstan's has unexpectedly served in a minor and unofficial capacity as a training center for purposes of recruitment. This phenomenon of unofficial recruitment could conceivably occur wherever several programs, such as the Job Corps Training Centers, are begun on a vast scale. There is the problem, expressed by some staff members at St. Wulstan's, that their experience is too specialized and limits their looking for less specialized nursing positions.

✑§ *DISCHARGE DATA* §✑

All patients admitted to the rehabilitation hospital are in the status of voluntary admissions. Some were certified, or committed by the courts, at the onset of their illness. Their status was changed from committed to voluntary several years before their rehabilitation was considered, rather than when they were admitted to St. Wulstan's.

The patient population of the rehabilitation hospital is smaller than that at traditional mental hospitals. This is in accordance with the present British trend toward reducing the size of new hospitals. There is little reason to believe that larger institutions would better serve the poor in adapting this plan to their plight. St. Wulstan's can accommodate 261 patients. Approximately 44 per cent of the patients are women and 56 per cent are men. Many of these patients have been hospitalized two decades or longer before admission.

During the three-year period of operation there were 108 discharges of patients who remained out of the hospital, excluding multiple discharges, or those patients who returned and were discharged more than once. Fifty-four of these patients went to open, or unsupervised, employment arranged before discharged to sheltered employment, fourteen were discharged to industrial rehabilitation units, and eleven were discharged fit for open employment—though none was arranged—and twelve were discharged unfit for employment.

These data do not reflect in any way the efficiency or value of the program because (1) the cases of multiple discharges were largely due to the patients leaving for temporary employment and being readmitted for lodgings until further work was available, sometimes at the same placement and (2) some readmissions represented premature employment placements where further rehabilitation seemed necessary but the patient wished to leave.

THE HOSPITAL/FACTORY IDEOLOGY

The ideology of the rehabilitation hospital staff involves the purpose and function of the hospital and the selection and discharge of its patients. The purpose of the hospital, as set forth by the administration, is to deal as effectively as possible with the growing number of long-term hospitalized and unemployed patients who languish in the parent hospitals. This does not mean that the patients selected are not on an active treatment regimen in the parent hospital; however, a reduction of the population in the overcrowded parent hospitals makes these institutions more effective in treating those patients who remain. With this incentive the parent-hospital staff is impelled to focus upon and review patients' assets for rehabilitation as quickly as possible. Of course, the nature of the parent hospitals determines to some extent the number of transfers to the rehabilitation hospital. Some of the parent hospitals have more active rehabilitation programs than others and consequently have a smaller number of candidates for the rehabilitation hospital. This fact was partly responsible for the inability to select a control group of parent-hospital patients in the studies reported in Chapter 5.

The hospital ideology as expressed by the staff contains a careful separation between treatment and rehabilitation. Such a distinction is important in rehabilitating the poor. Treatment is a forerunner of less supervised rehabilitation in caring for the patient in the hospital. This approach is in contrast to the problem of differentiating between treatment and rehabilitation as described by Rapoport (1960). Treatment is conceived as altering psychodynamics, and rehabilitation deals with the role enactment of the patient.

The primary function of the rehabilitation hospital is to train and release long-term patients to open employment and eventual return to the community. This is the most desired result, but a secondary function is recognized as equally important. The rehabilitation hospital creates other channels of possible placements that were not considered feasible for the patient while he was in the parent hospital. The rehabilitation hospital can be a zone of transition for the patient, where patients can be evaluated for transfer to institutions for the subnormal, if an intellectual deficit is the major problem, or to other institutions, if other types of continued care are needed. This role, which such a hospital could play, could be immeasurably valuable if adapted to the restoration of the poor. The rehabilitation hospital, then, has an assessment function. Initially, the belief was that patients would be discharged outright to employment. However, a much more complicated plan, allowing for day patients and temporary employment, has evolved.

An important aspect of the ideology articulated by every facet of the program is to anticipate the patients' vocational and adjustment needs. A highly practical approach in the choice of vocational training and the establishment of training methods is essential. One example of this practicality is the cooking classes that the hospital conducts. These classes are made up of patients who are being prepared for living in the hostel within the hospital, who intend to cook for themselves in lodgings with kitchen facilities, who are seeking domestic employment where this skill is required and will enhance their ability to obtain employment, or who are housewives or single women needing this skill to care for their family or relatives after discharge.

Fulfilling every patient's need is obviously impossible. However, in the employment area, an effort is made to place him in a work program where his interests and skills appear to be appropriate. Studies appear to indicate that return to the parent hospital is brought about by the patient's not focusing on any particular employment opportunity or goal, having unrealistic inspirations that he cannot abandon, or exhibiting antisocial behavior so flagrantly and persistently that the hospital community is unable to contain or tolerate him. This last point is generally held by the rehabilitation hospital staff to be a factor, but this opinion is not fully supported by our data. In some cases, however, disorganized behavior is responsible for the patient's having to return to the rehabilitation hospital after finding and then losing employment. It is a part of the hospital's ideology to take up the task again and to work with these patients at the level they had reached before they were employed.

Phenathiazines and other drugs are often given to patients in psychiatric hospitals for their better management, and, although the intent of the staff is not always so, the effect is the dulling and truncating of experience for the patient. An aspect of the ideology of the rehabilitation hospital is to discover, wherever possible, the explicit action of a single drug on the patient's behavior. Therefore, combinations of drugs are often discontinued when the patient enters as a new admission. This withdrawal of all drugs for a short period of time, in effect, frees the environmental factors to operate unimpeded. An evaluation of the patient is also possible without the need to pay close attention to the combined drug effects. Another significant part of the ideology of the rehabilitation hospital is to encourage the assistance of community members—particularly those who live in the vicinity of the hospital gate. These people are actively invited to call on the hospital authorities and to discuss the behavior of patients they have observed—not as informers but as those who share a common interest with the hospital staff.

The rating scales are a part of the formal ideology as described in the hospital procedural pamphlet that will be discussed later. This emphasis on ratings implies that the more rated information obtained about a patient, the more this greater knowledge will serve to help the patient on his way to improvement. In the process, incidentally, the staff members become quite sophisticated as raters.

Although originally no time limit was set at St. Wulstan's for the patient's rehabilitation, the initial plan was to work with each person for two years before terminating rehabilitation efforts. After it soon became apparent that some patients would require longer stays than this, the staff felt it wise to assess the period of time beyond the two-year period that the more deteriorated patients would require before some change occurred. Rehabilitation, then, was not conceived to be a relatively brief affair in the hospital's ideology. This was particularly true considering the long period of hospitalization—approximately twelve years—that the patients admitted at the beginning of the program required.

If a patient must be returned to the parent hospital, he is not readmitted to the rehabilitation hospital. The ethical reason for this policy or aspect to the rehabilitation ideology is clear. It enables another candidate to benefit from the experience at St. Wulstan's.

⋘§ ORGANIZATIONAL STRUCTURE §⋙

The organization of the rehabilitation hospital is geared to the needs of the patients and to the continual productivity of the institution. The hospital is organized in four separate units, each composed of a different number of blocks. Each unit is designated by official color names of "Grey," "Red," "Blue," and "Gold." Although these names were arbitrarily chosen, they fit well into the hospital decor. The three "living blocks," or wards, assigned to each unit have a door of the appropriate color. Colored doors permit quick and easy identification by the visitors and confused patients, and the hospital has a less monotonous appearance than the blocks might otherwise convey.

Patients living in the Grey Unit work in the Grey Unit workshop, and so on. The nursing staff supervise the patients during the day in the workshops in three shifts. There is a permanent night staff on duty in four of the six Grey and Blue Unit wards; a patrol nurse visits one Grey, one Blue, and three Red Unit wards, but Gold Unit patients are unsupervised during the night. One ward in Grey, Blue, and Gold is assigned to women, and the next two in the row are the Grey Unit for men, with 20 beds in each. The Red Unit has two wards for women, one for men. This pattern of alternation between men's and women's living quarters continues through the twelve blocks in the living area.

The physician superintendent and the registrar, both psychiatrists, along with each unit staff plan the programs for the patients in the Grey and Blue Units. The chief consultant, also a psychiatrist, and another trainee psychiatrist, handle these duties for Red and Gold Units. This division presents difficulties, but these are not too cumbersome because of the proximity of the units and the meetings conjointly between the unit staffs. To an outside observer, this arrangement might suggest two hospitals if this close relationship of daily contact did not exist. All members of the professional staff, including the superintendent, are officially assigned to one of the units for the purpose of meeting with patients in their group meetings. Post-hospitalization appointments on an out-patient basis are administered by the chief consultant without regard to the unit from which the patient was discharged. In practice, most patients are discharged from Gold Unit. Family interviews are held by the social workers who are also assigned to the units, one worker to each of the Grey-Blue and Red-Gold combinations.

There is no reason to believe that drastic changes would be necessary to adapt this organization to the poverty victim. Appropriate changes could be made in the professional staff.

The staff-to-patient ratio of the rehabilitation hospital is one to three. Each unit has its own charge nurses, staff nurses, nursing assistants, and orderlies. Among the nursing staff the ratio of men to women is approximately two to one. The role of the orderlies, three to each unit, is to clean the entrance of the workshops and to prepare tea twice daily for the patients and staff who take their beverage in the workshop. The staff nurse supervises the patients and fills out various reports. The charge nurses have general supervision of the unit workshops, and distribution of labor and materials. The overall deployment of labor is handled by the personnel officer. The negotiation for contracts is handled by the industrial supervisor.

In keeping with the factory atmosphere that prevails throughout the hospital, the personnel officer is responsible for the patients only as personnel, or workers. He can act as the industrial supervisor when the latter is on leave. Neither of these offices is found in a traditional hospital setting. The introduction of these offices into the hospital makes rehabilitation possible and makes the hospital less a hospital and more of a factory. The role of industrial supervisor is that of a plant manager. The employees filling these two staff positions not only should be in accord with the hospital ideology, that is, thinking along the same lines as to what the hospital/factory has to offer the patient—or poverty victim—but also should be personally compatible.

The units are structured in such a way that after a three-week assessment of the new patient's assets and liabilities and—less important—his treatment in the Grey Unit, he can either be transferred directly to the highest level of work responsibility in the Gold Unit or be channeled to the intermediate step of the Red Unit. If a problem arises and the patient is unable to cope with the demands of either Red or Gold Unit, he is sent to the Blue Unit. The presence of the Blue Unit is a recognition of the fact that all mental hospitals require a place where the demands are less on the patient but continued, active rehabilitation is necessary. A shift in the living arrangements appropriate to each block follows each transfer.

The patients in the Grey, Blue, and Red Units work from 9:00 A.M. to 12 noon, and from 2:00 P.M. to 5:00 P.M. each weekday, or a thirty-hour week. The patients in the Gold Unit, who enjoy much less supervision, work from 8:30 A.M. to either 12:00 noon or 12:30 P.M., and from 1:30 P.M. to 5:30 P.M., for approximately forty hours a week. The hours are increased in the Gold Unit to prepare the patient for factory conditions. A few patients, of course, express some initial complaints before being assimilated into the new routine. Less supervision in the living area acts as a compensation, along with more hours in which to earn additional money.

Most of the patients are assigned to the workshops, but some have special assignments to working parties, such as to the gardeners, who maintain the hospital vegetable garden and grounds, or to the ancillary staff of the hospital. For example, the patients perform much of the routine office work of the clerical section, which keeps the hospital accounts. They also maintain laundry lists, and invoices for the industrial account, which contains the proceeds of sales from the factory. Other patients are assigned to such work as painters, domestic section, and tilemakers.

The patients have their own Sports and Social Club, which is its official title, and their activities are casually supervised by the physical-training instructor. The canteen is open for patients' use only in the evenings and during the noon hours while they are not working. Some of the produce that the patients raise is sold through the canteen. The hairdresser for women is open during the day. Once a fortnight each woman is allowed a shampoo and set by appointment, which she herself makes; she is permitted the same before her discharge or a job interview. A barber comes to the hospital one evening a week for the men. The hairdresser also offers informal classes in beauty treatment and proper cosmetic use.

Weekends are free for the patients between the hours of 6:00 P.M. on Friday and 9:45 P.M. on Sunday. Leaves during working hours are not encouraged but may be granted under special circumstances. All special outings planned by the patients through their Sports and Social Club are held on the weekends.

During the three-week assessment period, evaluation and timed tests are administered to the patients. These are, for the most part, situation tests specific to the kinds of work offered in the hospital. During this period the staff members of each unit also fill out the work report. The report is continued as long as the patient is in the hospital; if the hospital patient has a steady but temporary job, his outside employer fills out the report.

The hospital social workers make inquiries about the patient's living relatives and his vocational history and file their report in much the same way as social workers working with welfare recipients. The psychologist evaluates the patient according to his requirements for social re-education and makes a general intellectual assessment. A test is administered to the patient in the clerical section if he has a history of this type of work in his background. The patient's financial status is reported by the hospital's finance department. All these data such as intelligence and family resources are disseminated and discussed at the first meeting, which is called the "intake review." The registrar also discusses medication at this time. A tentative plan for the period of stay the patient may require is set up and the patient is informed of this fact. This period may be one year and eighteen months to two years. The second review meeting for the patient may be four to six months, depending upon the projected length of stay. For example, a patient whose expected stay is one year will be evaluated again after a comparatively short time. All subsequent meetings after the second review meeting are held in the unit in which the patient is being rehabilitated. The projected stay may be revised at any time. Every patient is reviewed at least twice yearly. The lay staff working with the patient at the time attend the meetings and report on his progress.

At the time of the intake review, the patients are also given a grade designation. A few clinic patients are given a Grade 3 status; the number of these patients is no more than six to seven at any time. They have only the freedom of the grounds because of past behavioral problems. Other patients are Grade 2, with privileges for passes only if they ask leave from some member of the staff. Ninety per cent of the patients, however, are Grade 1 and have no restrictions whatsoever when they are not working.

It is anticipated that such a grading system would be dispensed with if the program was adapted to a poverty group. Adapting the program to other types of people, such as criminals, would call for more careful evaluation. This topic is further explored in a later chapter.

The patients are selected for admission in part by the parent hospital staff. They select a group of patients for St. Wulstan's physician superintendent to interview when he calls at the hospital. These are routine visits; he makes one each month to one of the parent hospitals. He follows a prescribed schedule of questions, including a standardized mental-status examination (Wing, 1961). He fills out a rating chart assessing the nature of the ward environment from which the patient is selected. Along with other information, this chart includes the type of privileges accorded the patient. A behavior report (Wing, 1960) is completed by the nurse in the ward from which the patient comes. The selected patients, who usually agree to the transfer to St. Wulstan's, are transported there by the sending hospital. If there are patients to be returned to that particular hospital, this is done at the same time. Selected patients are free to refuse admission to the rehabilitation hospital if they wish to do so; their families also have the right to intervene.

The Clinic

As the rehabilitation hospital structure evolved, every effort was made to create an environment as unlike the patient's previous one and as close to life outside the hospital as possible. This principle of substituting a learning environment for a non-learning one is the same for poverty victims and the unemployed mentally ill. In the case of St. Wulstan's, therefore, a treatment clinic in the hospital was established to house temporarily those patients who had become highly disturbed. These people may be transferred from the units to the clinic for a brief period of time, or they may be brought to the clinic from outside placement on a job before they are ready again to live in the units. Those working in the hospital often request moving to the clinic rather than wait for the staff to make the suggestion. Those patients coming from an outside job who profit from treatment in the clinic usually resume the same assignment they held in the hospital prior to their upset, if the staff feels that the assignment did not contribute to their condition. They may even continue their work from the clinic if this is felt to be beneficial. Usually, however, playing the sick role, or the role of the patient, is more advisable, and they are given every opportunity to convalesce without having demands placed upon them. Personality regression is discouraged; for this reason, the clinic patient does not perform manual arts techniques, since they apparently promote such regression in this population. Instead, the patient spends most of his time in meetings or in doing light chores to maintain the premises.

The function of the clinic in the hospital's rehabilitation programs has been stated as follows:[4] (1) The clinic serves to differentiate the fit to work from the unfit to work; this separation, therefore, is made much more clearly than in the traditional system where psychiatric care is given in the ward. Since nurses leave the wards in the clinic system there is no one to care for the "unfit" patient in his ward. (2) Wards relieved of the sickest patients appear much less like hospitals and more like ordinary living quarters for those

---

[4] Personal communication from Dr. Roger Morgan.

who remain in them. (3) The staff and patients begin to think of those who are not in the clinic as being well because they are working. This expectation of normal working behavior serves to alter the patients' self-image. (4) A patient can decide to see the psychiatrist any morning and go to the clinic for a consultation—with permission from the charge nurse. Making decisions is thus encouraged by this arrangement.

Obviously, all medical treatment cannot be made available at the clinic. If the patients need other than first aid or psychiatric treatment—such as radiograms or gynecological services—they are transported to a nearby infirmary by ambulance.

The Hostel

A small hostel accommodating six female patients is located in the hospital. Such a living arrangement has also been called a "quarter house," as distinct from a "halfway house," and its function is usually considered as a preparatory step toward the patient's living in the "halfway house" (Mason *et al.,* 1963). Two of the patients who reside in the hostel perform the cooking and domestic chores while the remaining four patients are employed in the community. Problems sometimes arise when a highly competent person performing the purchasing and cooking duties wishes to leave and no available person is qualified to take her place.

All hospital patients other than those in the clinic and the hostel must exert an effort to attend the midday meal in the common dining room, which is located in a block separate from the units. Male and female patients eat at the same tables—a feature that provides a more normal social interaction between the sexes. Few patients behave irresponsibly. Breakfast, tea, and supper are served in the wards.

The recreation and television facilities are in a separate block from the units. In this way optimal movement to and from the living area is facilitated in the evening hours.

The patients are free to purchase limited items in the canteen, but larger items such as clothing must be bought in the community.

Wages

During his assessment period the patient is paid ten shillings, or one dollar and twenty cents, a week, and he is told that he may earn much more after his initial period is finished and he has been assigned to his job.

Patients in the workshops are permitted to earn up to £1. 19s. 11d., or approximately four dollars and eighty cents, during any single week. If they earn more than this figure, they forfeit their sickness benefits and become liable to pay contributions to the National Health Insurance. The hospital staff also decided to abide by this ceiling in order to encourage even greater earnings by the patients after discharge. They are paid in cash and encouraged to bank their savings in the community. If it is necessary for them to go to the clinic, they receive two-thirds the pay they earned during the last three working weeks as sick pay. Patients may also receive sixteen shillings, or approximately one dollar and ninety cents, as sickness benefits from the National Health Insurance weekly as long as they are hospitalized. Some patients, because of unemployment or failure to contribute weekly to the National Health Insurance and/or register for National Assistance before they were hospitalized, do not receive this benefit. It is part of the function of the re-education classes to explain this to them. The benefits are deposited in the administration block along with funds received from other sources outside the hospital/factory. More often, however, the patient is encouraged to open an account in the local post office savings bank.

Evidence shows that piece rate as a type of payment acts as a greater motivator—ability held constant—than time or bonus rate (Wyatt, 1934). Piece rate dominates the pay rate of the rehabilitation hospital in order to maximize motivation. Piece rate also has a relatively higher discriminating value in comparing patients' performance or the performance of a patient over time. If the patient is from a particular unit and is assigned to a working party or to the clerical section, he is paid a flat rate per hour. Assessment for increased earnings is made by the supervisor in that section. There is a wide range of jobs in the working party category; besides those named earlier are those of woodcutter, upholsterer, window cleaner, car washer, pipe fitter, laundry worker, and kitchen worker. This category also includes the unit orderlies. The wages may vary from three to six shillings (thirty-six to seventy-two cents) a day for a five-day week.

Funds

The maintenance of the rehabilitation hospital requires more than one account. Consequently, the management of the hospital and the earnings from the factory are maintained separately. Staff salaries are managed through the hospital's exchequer account maintained by the Ministry of Health. The amenities account for the patients is separate. Into this account go the payments for services rendered and goods supplied by the rehabilitation hospital. Ten per cent of this fund is placed in the exchequer account for overhead costs. A part of the balance from the overhead costs is paid to the patients directly. If this payment does not absorb this balance, the additional money is used for a variety of purposes, all of which further the patients' rehabilitation, such as resettling the patient after discharge until he receives his first earnings, giving a small grant to each patient going on an annual holiday for one week or more (this procedure will be explained later), paying sick benefits to patients temporarily unable to work in the hospital, as well as part of the fee for patients who are taking adult-education instruction in the evenings (for example, cooking classes in the community college), buying new equipment, and paying patients with low weekly earnings.

Some of the patients work outside the hospital while living in one of the units. If a balance remains from this source beyond that which the patients are permitted to receive while hospitalized, such money is placed in the industrial account, a section of the amenities account. Most of these patients are domestically employed either in the community or with families of the hospital staff. The National Health Service policy dictates that a patient working full-time but still residing in the hospital must pay the hospital three-quarters of his earnings up to a maximum of £4. 15s. 0d. (U.S. $11.40) a week for board and room. This policy is not easily accepted by some of those who have been in the rehabilitation hospital for a long time and are asked to reimburse the hospital for those amenities that they once enjoyed without payment.

≼§ COMMUNICATION STRUCTURE §≽

In the same manner that the hospital's organizational structure changed as needs arose, its communication evolved. For purposes of analysis, communication can be divided into that between hospital staff members and patients, and among members of each group, and that between the hospital and community.

A permanent record of the policy formulated by the hospital staff, and the development of the organizational structure is contained in a book called the "bible." A written record, which visitors may read, it describes the duties of the various staff members, the handling of the patients' funds, the scheduling of meetings and conferences, and all necessary information on the maintenance of the hospital. It also contains samples of the standard schedule used by the physician superintendent and other rating materials. This record is under constant revision by members of the policy committee, which holds frequent routine meetings. The copies of the book are kept in the hospital library.

It is from the policy committee—essentially a highly democratic, intrahospital communication source—that many of the formal staff decisions emanate. The committee is composed of the hospital secretary, his secretary, the physician superintendent, the consultants, the top nursing staff, the senior psychologist, and elected representatives from the units and the ancillary staff. The committee is separated further into various working subcommittees, the members of which are expected to attend meetings when they are called. Members of the policy committee are encouraged to meet their "constituents" and to explain policy changes. They are, in turn, the spokesmen for the members of their unit staff and are responsible for relaying to the committee these people's reactions to decisions.

A workshop newsletter published each week is another example of direct and permanent forms of communication. It lists the complete, weekly production of the workshops and other hospital sections, such as the concrete factory. This newsletter reflects the large number of contracts that St. Wulstan's holds and may list twenty-six firms or other hospitals in the area that it serves. A single edition may enumerate twenty different outlets for the assembled, repaired, or fabricated articles upon which the patients have worked. The outlets may be specific firms or individuals either in the community or among the staff members themselves. The types of work are generally subsumed under the titles of "contracts," "subcontracts," or "service." The newsletter also publishes each week the names of patients who carried out the assigned task of "punching in" at the workshop time clocks; it also publishes the names of those who demonstrated an inability to do so or who were early or late in clocking. Approval or disapproval is therefore placed in the "public realm," and the knowledge of results of effort is not only presented to the patient but to his peers. Finally, a note is made of the employment movement of the patients. If one should lose his job, possible reasons for the loss are also printed. Other related news of interest, such as leaves, net earnings, and visitors from the firms for which the hospital does work, is included. The newsletter is signed by the personnel officer and typed and distributed by the patients assigned to the clerical section.

Also helping to facilitate intrahospital communication is the Forum, a formal group meeting held monthly, in which all members of the staff are invited to participate. This brief meeting serves to communicate ideas and attitudes on hospital issues among the ancillary, nursing, and administrative staffs.

Often the hospital domain of the nurse in a psychiatric hospital is circumscribed by the ward or, in the case of St. Wulstan's, to the work area and living area. Here all charge nurses are given a month's orientation in the distribution of the patients' finances and the hospital accounts. These sessions are conducted in the administration block by the finance officer. Such a procedure considerably reduces the isolation of the finance section from the rest of the hospital. This isolation is also lessened by having a member of the nursing staff and a finance officer share in paying the patients in their unit workshops.

Another source of information exchange is the review committee meeting. These meetings are remarkably uniform and yet permit changes of viewpoint about a patient. This combination of continuity and flexibility in thinking about a patient on the part of the unit staffs is possible for these three reasons: (1) the occasional change of unit-staff membership but, more important, the interchange of duties within the nursing staff; (2) the use of continued behavior and work reports; (3) the essentially unvarying procedure followed at each review meeting between the units.

Communication received from the patients' relatives may be shared in the review meetings. However, opinions of the family members about the patient do not influence the staff's evaluation. Greater weight is given the ratings received from past and present employers. The patients do not rate one another. The staff depends primarily upon the ratings rather than upon family members' evaluations in order to counteract the often negative view of the patient that may grow among relatives who misunderstand. It is thought that this would be particularly true with regard to more successful relatives evaluating the poverty victim.

Intrahospital communication, of course, cannot leave out the patient. Meetings among patients and staff closely follow the unit pattern of the program. Each unit and the clinic have a formal meeting once a week, for which the patients take minutes. Spontaneous expression is encouraged and there is ordinarily no prearranged agenda. Each unit is also divided into four small groups of both male and female patients. Meetings of these small groups are informally conducted on another day of the week by the charge nurse or staff nurses. The nature of the interaction among the patients in these groups and their level of social withdrawal vary and depend upon the approach of the nurse assigned to the group. Every unit patient is therefore involved in two meetings a week. Attendance is voluntary.

There are special weekly evening meetings of a formal nature for clinic patients. Though patients from outside the clinic are permitted to attend these meetings, their presence is sometimes a point of controversy. The meetings, however, are rarely dominated by a patient outside the clinic group, and the minutes are always taken by a clinic patient. The staff recognize, nevertheless, that all too frequently outside patients may attend who derive satisfaction from controlling meetings of this type.

There has been no investigation as to which type of group meeting is most attractive to patients. Some apparently respond better in some meetings than in others. Others maintain a similar level of withdrawal in all types of meetings. Some patients form new friendships or, at least, at first, maintain contact with those who have been admitted with them from the same parent hospital. These relationships are encouraged by the staff, even to the extent of formal marital engagements. This encouragement depends, however, upon the patients' condition; even so, marriage counseling between the parties concerned sometimes becomes necessary.

Relationships of an emotional intensity may have their detrimental effect on patients, as the following example shows. Two patients had been seeing one another for several weeks. It became necessary, however, to transfer the man to the clinic for a time because of a physical ailment. This transfer was so upsetting to the woman that she visited the clinic each day to see that the clinic staff had not killed her friend. Close relationships also have their hazards when one of the patients must be returned to the parent hospital. Sometimes two women will choose to share accommodations when they leave the hospital. It has been observed that one is usually more intelligent and less dependent than the other. This may be an extension of a work relationship that began in the hospital. Topics like these—plans for leaving and so on—are discussed in the patients' groups.

Another aspect of the patients' life is of vital concern in fostering high morale at the hospital. For a three-week period, thirty-six patients each week enjoy a holiday at a nearby resort hotel. They are accompanied by four staff members, who give them little direct supervision. Tape-recorded impressions made by the patients indicate a positive response to these holidays. These outings also give the staff a chance to observe the patients in a relatively unstructured situation and to discuss with them their attitudes toward the rehabilitation hospital while they are away from its environment. Other trips are also arranged by the patients under the indirect supervision of the physical training instructor. (The cost of these outings was explained in the section dealing with hospital funds.) These outings are excursions into the community and lead us into the topic of hospital-community communication.

The most important channels of communication between community and hospital are the industrial supervisor, the personnel officer, the superintendent, and the resettlement officer, who visits the hospital as a representative of the Ministry of Labor and is an expert on employment conditions in the community. The social workers (who in this hospital are also psychiatric nurses) are also sources of communication between the hospital and the community, and handle many placement problems.

The industrial supervisor contacts industry and insures delivery of factory goods. The personnel officer assists in the work follow-up by asking the employers in the hiring firms or at the individual placements to report the progress of the patient on the work report form. The superintendent is active in community affairs; he discussed the implications of the rehabilitation hospital with interested professional and business people in the community prior to its opening. He also helps plan the annual open house at the hospital. The social workers actively find lodgings for the patients in the community and contact groups or organizations that might help to place patients. An interesting example of the social workers' assistance is the placement of members of St. Wulstan's only minority ethnic group in Polish clubs, which have been established to help assimilate these people into the community.

Many hospitals show filmstrips to their personnel as a form of communication between hospital and community. In the hospital/factory these films frequently deal not only with disease and treatment but with production management, cost accounting, and such topics.

ANALYSIS OF WORK

The patients work both inside and outside the hospital. Although the number of the patients working out of the hospital fluctuates, the nature of their jobs is mainly unskilled. On one representative day, for example, thirty-three patients were working out: twenty-one were performing housekeeping jobs, seven were gardeners, two general laborers, one, a factory worker, one, a gas station attendant, and one, a kitchen assistant.

The nucleus of the hospital/factory, for both patients and staff, is the workshop. It is here that initial assessments of the patients occur and from where most are discharged. The physical description of the workshops has already been given. Here, we must understand the nature of the work in these shops.

Many considerations go into a decision to accept or not accept the types of work that the hospital contracts. Some of these decisions are related to the work force, that is, to the patients themselves. Here are some guidelines I have formulated:

1. Some work should be intellectually challenging, but most of the work should cater to the assembly-line and piecework model, and be geared to the person of low-average intelligence. (This is sometimes difficult for a nurse of superior intelligence to accept.)

2. There should be at least one job without a deadline attached to it in the contract—one which can be given to the most deteriorated patients safely. It will be that job upon which the workshop relies when other contracts have been completed and there is little otherwise to occupy the patients' time. Reclaiming materials and stripping telephone units are examples.

3. The distribution of types of work should be roughly similar to that found in the community to which the patients will be returning. At the same time, the quantity of output should not pose a threat to the firms in the community.

4. The work should include such jobs as shop clerking and stocking, which are found in a variety of firms. The work should not be too specialized.

5. The materials for the work should not be too bulky to be transported on the hospital vehicles or packed and handled by patients.

6. Some work should be such that more than one person works alongside another, and there is an opportunity to talk about it while the work is in progress.

7. The work should be of a type where production manage-

ment is possible, where quality control can be maintained by the patients to some extent, and where improvements in efficiency and quality can be introduced by an enterprising staff or by the patients. As a result, morale is improved for both patient and staff member.

8. All work should be of the sort that can be rated on the work report in which some discriminating appraisal of change in performance—besides for output—can be made.

9. All work should be meaningful and socially valuable. This point concerns the value of the patient of performing volunteer work after hours (as some patients are occasionally asked to do) or of constructing items to be given as contributions to the public for a particular fund or charity. Some patients respond to the altruism of such a situation. Doing this kind of work for charitable causes does not carry with it the idea of working toward supporting oneself after discharge, and the patient may engage in this work as a pastime. At the same time, such activities may be enjoyable diversions from the routine of hospital life. It is for these reasons that these tasks are better left to the older patient, to whom it would be cruel to create an illusion that he is working toward a discharge when, in reality, his physical condition requires a continuation of nursing care.

The large number of varied activities enables the patients to be placed on individual tasks or in assembly-line groups situations. Should a patient show extreme motor retardation, placing him between faster workers on an assembly-line job often produces some change in his speed of performance without affecting his accuracy. Some tasks require detailed work; others require strength as well as precision. If a patient should drink too much in the bar provided for them at the supervised dances or while he is in town, no restrictive measures are taken, but he is expected to work the following day.

Despite a certain homogeneity of some of the tasks between the units, a difference is apparent in the general atmosphere. In the Grey Unit, adaptability as well as productivity is measured. There appears to be more activity there, along with the radio music that is common to all of the units. Patients in the Gold Unit go quietly about their individual jobs and are more responsible for the appearance of their unit. The patients in the Blue Unit experience much less change in their routine than do patients in any of the other units, and they work to a greater extent on standard items. Here, super-vision is greater than in the Gold Unit and there is much more random activity and pacing. Red Unit is similar to Grey Unit in its activity, with several assembly-line conditions. Here, the staff works side by side with the patients, in contrast to Grey Unit, where the staff carefully supervise the patients and only occasionally stop to show them how the work is done, and to Gold Unit, where the staff are more like consultants. In the "higher" units, many patients ar-rive early and set about their work promptly. Latecomers are more characteristic of the Blue Unit. No attempt is made to seek out the patient who has not reported, nor is discipline given to the patient who argues in the workshop. These situations are discussed in the group meetings if they involve the work productivity of that unit; or the psychiatrist and charge nurse may consult with the patient about the problem.

There is another aspect of hospital/factory life that is gov-erned by the nature of the work performed there—clothing and uni-forms. The work is often such that would soil clothing easily. All patients are supplied, on the day of admission, therefore, with a full kit of clothing, including protective clothes to be worn only in the work areas. Members of the nursing staff are issued blazers, navy blue for the male nurses, to be worn outside the workshops, and the same protective clothing as the patients while working. Professional staff and lay staff wear no characteristic apparel. The supervisors of the work parties wear the protective clothing.

The wearing of street clothing or work clothing by the staff is a form of non-verbal communication. It "tells" the patient that it is no longer necessary for him to be surrounded by immaculate white uniforms. The nurse and the patient can be as unclean as the job permits or demands. Except for the clinic, where white is worn, the hospital appears even more like a factory, and this is an impor-tant feature of this rehabilitation approach.

RESOCIALIZATION AND DISCHARGE

Socialization in this context means a re-education of the patient in the conduct and fulfillment of everyday societal expecta-tions. Other definitions of socialization should not be confused with our meaning here. Our definition does not imply, for example, correcting antisocial behavior, such as stealing, or the development process of learning social norms in a given culture, such as learning that it is considered wrong to steal. Although resocialization in the rehabilitation hospital is not confined to the special section designated for the purpose,[5] this section is, nevertheless, important to formalize the instruction in this area and to assess the new patient in his need for such training.

Patients in this special section are seen by the senior psychologist and the physical training instructor for retraining, so they may cope with the problems they may encounter after discharge and so they may also improve their general appearance with group exercise. Patients found to be deficient in the unit review meetings are formed into classes for retraining and, wherever possible, are taken from the workshops in a manner that will cause a minimum of disruption to the production flow. Taking these patients necessitates close liaison with the workshop staffs and the personnel officer. Strict attendance is kept, and the workshops are kept informed as to the time and place of the retraining classes. An hourly wage is worked out on the basis of the patient's individual rate of earnings and is given him for the time he spends in the classes.

Assessment and education are given in the following areas: physical hygiene, first aid, use of the telephone banking procedures, computing paychecks, posting and mailing letters, telling time, planning journeys, filling out job applications and applications for health insurance, budgeting living expenses, and writing sick notes after gaining employment. Various devices, such as mock telephones and charts, are used for this learning purpose. Role-playing interviews are arranged for those patients who have trouble overcoming the difficulties involved and applying for jobs.

At some point, the patient is hopefully considered ready for discharge. Many staff members are involved in the discharge of the patient, including the resettlement officer, who maintains an office on the premises. There is no system of transitional trials, but ex-

---

[5] There is an analysis of this section in Chapter 5, with details in Appendix G.

tended leave while the patient is looking for work is possible. A direct discharge is routine. Before it is completed, the unit-charge nurse, with the patient's help, goes over a checklist of items that should be covered before he leaves, such as handing in clothing or a last visit to the social worker. This procedure communicates the finality of the rehabilitation relationship the patient has enjoyed with the hospital and the personnel. Arrangements are made for the patient to see the chief consultant on the weekends if out-patient follow-up seems necessary.

⋘ TWO CASE HISTORIES ⋙

Rarely is a book on rehabilitation written without the inclusion of a case history, and usually one which is classified as successful. Some books report several histories to illustrate the various avenues rehabilitation can take. We will limit ourselves, however, to one case which was termed successful—although the patient has not yet worked a year outside the hospital—and to another where success was less definitive. We will primarily emphasize the patients' careers in the rehabilitation hospital; we will discuss their case histories before their admission only where they are relevant to rehabilitation.

The first case concerns a middle-aged, unmarried woman who had spent nine years in the parent hospital before coming to St. Wulstan's. She was above average in intelligence and had held a responsible position a few years prior to her admission. At one time she was interested in a man, but this relationship ended with a humiliating experience and he married someone else. Extremely disappointed, she began to live a solitary life and occasionally visited her mother. Her job, however, went well until she began experiencing shortness of breath, heart palpitations, and extreme anxiety when in crowds. Fearing for her own life and what she might do to herself, she obtained admission to a parent hospital and was given various tranquilizers. No attempt was made to find her employment, and she became even more socially withdrawn than before—preferring to read books from the library rather than engaging in any of the hospital activities.

She finally came to the rehabilitation hospital as an unselected patient and was very miserable for the first few weeks. She made many self-derogatory remarks and physical complaints. Her highest work scores were obtained in the domestic section, and she was given this assignment in preference to the workshop, where she complained of the noise and was obviously under continual tension. However, as soon as she was put in the domestic section, she failed to distinguish herself, except that she continued to be punctual and had—as throughout her hospitalization—consistently good behavior ratings. She would put the equipment in the wrong closet in the wrong building after she had finished with it. She was unable to hang out washing correctly when working for a member of the staff's family. It finally came to light that she had made her initial good ratings in the domestic section because she was able to follow the other patients and to pattern her work responsibilities after them. This did not carry over when she was given something to do on her own. It was clear that her mother had previously done such work for her and when she lived alone, it was left undone.

For a short time, she was assigned to the workshop. She seemed to perform most satisfactorily while checking the work of other patients. She would often stay after everyone else had finished for the day and compulsively go over what she had done. Her accuracy with figures suffered during the first evaluation in the clerical section, partly because she was being supervised and watched while she was working. When she was again placed in the clerical section and given more independence, she began to respond. So that she could take more responsibility of a social nature, she was given the task of preparing and serving the tea, and soon she was able to advise other patients about this procedure. She was promoted to Gold Unit and still went to the clerical section for her work. Lack of flexibility was one of her problems, so she was given several assignments of a clerical nature. She worked in the stockroom, for example, filing invoices. The most significant progress she made was in the hostel, where she continued her duties of serving tea to the others in the hostel and working in the clerical section. Another patient had taken over her tea-serving duties in the clerical section with her tutelage.

She formed a close attachment to another woman patient and began attending lectures in the community and reading books from the city library. When this friend found a job in a nearby city, she visited her on occasion. Eventually, a position in a small factory was found for her and, after hesitating and repeatedly asking staff members if she should take the job, she was accepted. On some occasions the anxiety during this period became so oppressive that upon her request she was permitted to spend a few days in the clinic.

She now shares an apartment with another patient working at the same factory—a woman somewhat like her former hospital friend. She is not free from anxieties, but she is able to perform many duties she thought impossible a few years ago. I recall that this patient once said to me, "How can you expect us to give up the green tranquillity of the rehabilitation hospital for the hell of a factory?" Despite these reservations, she was able to do just that.

This patient's appearance has altered only slightly since she was at St. Wulstan's. She wears flat heels and still has close-cropped hair, but she is able to tolerate a few cosmetics, which give her more color. Incidentally, she does not have the hirsutism, or hairiness, that characterizes some female patients regardless of their psychiatric diagnosis; as a result, depilatory measures were not taken at the hospital to make her appearance more attractive.

Our second case history concerns a man who was also middle-aged but of subnormal intelligence. His tests showed that he had an I.Q. of 63 and was also illiterate. He was admitted to St. Wulstan's after an acute episode of hearing voices condemning him; these abated only after several shock treatments in another parent hospital. Prior to coming to St. Wulstan's, he had been hospitalized for twelve years, a period broken only by three short visits to his parents. Periods of work in his history were sparse. He had done some menial chores around his father's grocery before securing a factory job, which consisted of cleaning the office and plant floors. During his assessment period he performed slowly and uninspiringly all of the tasks except those for which he had not been trained. Attempts at training him to do house painting or to work with the engineers were unsuccessful. This lack of success was not due to his psychotic outbursts—for he customarily showed little emotion of any kind—but was due, instead, to the slow pace at which he worked. He was also a source of irritation for some of the other patients who worked with him in the workshops. Placing him between two faster workers was to no avail, since under pressure he would go to the toilets or to the workshop kitchen where tea was made. He would smoke in one of these two areas of retreat. This behavior would disrupt the total work procedure. In conversations he responded only in monosyllables. His expression remained stony and unsmiling. During the two and a half years, accumulated evidence indicated that he required more carefully structured training—particularly re-education—than St. Wulstan's could give him.

In order to ascertain his capacity for learning, we placed him in the resocialization classes. Here, his scores increased with instruction, and they continued to increase for a few weeks following the end of the class of which he was a member. On the strength of this increase in his performance, the psychologist recommended placing him in a training institution for mental defectives.

An interview was arranged at the rehabilitation hospital with a staff member of a subnormal training school in an area close to the patient's home. The patient was placed on the waiting list for transfer when administratively feasible. Meanwhile, he continued the one assignment that he seemed to enjoy: cleaning an area of the rehabilitation hospital streets. He received the flat-rate payment for this work, which was supervised by the gardeners. Other staff members made a point to talk with him briefly while he worked, and he was soon able to sweep the gravel and debris in piles and to clean a large area in a reasonably short time.

This patient continued his training in another type of institution geared more to adult education for people very low in intelligence. Not all people of his intelligence are recommended for this type of placement, and many of them are able to find work, despite the handicap of illiteracy, after a period of rehabilitation at St. Wulstan's.

⋙ SUMMARY ⋘

In an effort to expand the facilities for rehabilitating the poor, we have turned our attention to a hospital approach that was founded for the long-term mental patient. In order to give to the reader as vivid a picture of the hospital/factory as possible and to make it come alive for him we traced its history and described its physical setting and construction. The relationship between hospital/factory and the parent hospitals from where the patients came was described. We analyzed its internal function and its relationship to the surrounding community by describing the various jobs the staff members held and the forms of communication that they have between themselves and with the community. Occasionally we mentioned possible implications these jobs and forms of communication had for helping the poverty victim. We described the wages and financial arrangements as a business venture and found that the staff salaries and wages of the patients were separate accounts. We described how special problems of National Assistance, such as Social Security, were handled. The fact that many of the patients had been out of the community from which they had originated for several years meant that many required special training, called "social re-education," and we described this program. What work the patients and staff nurses actually did was analyzed by means of some recommendations that can be viewed as benefiting all persons who have been demoralized by unemployment. Despite the highly structured environment that the hospital/factory presents, the patients may have quite different experiences during their rehabilitation, as our two case histories showed.

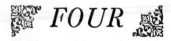

FOUR

The Hospital Factory

only upon those aspects of the hospital/factory that make it different from most other hospitals and treatment programs. Because promoters of these other programs emphasize the formation of small groups within the therapeutic community as a means of social support for the patient, we will also consider in this chapter the social psychology of small groups, and show the contrasts between these groups in the hospital/factory and those in another well-known ward program.

Our first task, however, is to compare the treatment of the mentally disturbed in the hospital/factory with their treatment in other mental institutions. We will make this comparison from the point of view of the staff member, whose work is an integral part of the rehabilitation program.

In this chapter we will compare the hospital/factory approach with other treatment programs, which have been described in the rehabilitation literature in detail that is beyond the scope of this book.[1] Here, we will concentrate

[1] See, for example, Colarelli, N. J. and S. M. Siegel, *Ward H: An Adventure in Innovation* (Princeton: Van Nostrand, 1966); Cumming, J. and Elaine Cumming, *Ego and Milieu: Theory and Practice of Environmental Therapy* (New York: Atherton, 1962); Fairweather, G. W. (ed.), *Social Psychology in Treating Mental Illness: An Experimental Approach* (New York: John Wiley, 1964); Kandel, D. B. and R. H. Williams, *Psychiatric Rehabilitation: Some Problems of Research* (New York: Atherton, 1964); Roth, J. A. and E. M. Eddy, *Rehabilitation for the Unwanted* (New York: Atherton, 1967).

⊷§ *ADVANTAGES AND DISADVANTAGES* §∾

The function of the rehabilitation hospital is quite different from that of the parent hospital; this difference requires amplification.

A number of points show how the rehabilitation hospital staff operates with distinct advantages. The staff of the rehabilitation hospital can select candidates for rehabilitation; the parent hospital staff, or any usual mental hospital staff, cannot. The structure of the rehabilitation hospital makes it a highly desirable place to work for those who wish to enjoy an unusual freedom from other commitments, a larger number of staff for a smaller number of patients, and an easy disposition of rehabilitation "rejects," or "failures." Dr. Morgan, the physician superintendent, credits the maintenance of a permissive atmosphere and a high level of expectation among the patients to their not having to live with those failures.

There are also disadvantages from the staff's point of view. Certain disadvantages stem from the democratic ideology and structure of the hospital: the lack of checks against irresponsible behavior, and the uncertainty of authority where no specific chain of command exists. There is also greater chance for one person being placed under divided authority.

Many details of the physical and organizational structure of St. Wulstan's were touched upon to show how needs of the staff and patients are met and their tensions reduced. The Staff Sports and Social Club, for example, fulfills a distinct need for affiliation among the staff members. The team spirit derived from the sports contests helps to reduce tension among them. They also share duties in the maintenance of the clubhouse, where they may enjoy informal meetings and organized activities. Some staff members take up community interests outside the hospital to offset the tendency toward institutionalization and social isolation fostered by life in the hospital. Once a year the staff present an amusement program for the patients, and help the patients in selecting both alcoholic and non-alcoholic refreshments for this event.

The rehabilitation hospital has the advantage of having two staff positions in special relationships between staff members and between patients. The Hospital Secretary has the task of easing intrastaff tensions and showing guidance in the staff's social affairs. His position, although outside the treatment team, has prestige and demands intimate knowledge of the philosophy and the financial maintenance of the hospital. The Personnel Officer plays a similar role, serving the patients instead of the staff. This officer is responsible for distribution of work and patient labor; he, too, enjoys a certain prestige among the patients. It is difficult to see how the hospital could carry on both work and diversion without these staff positions.

The work of the nurse is an example of how essentially the same professional people found in other types of institutions may perform different types of duties in the hospital/factory. The nurse becomes an expert at evaluating persons who will be employed in that particular type of employment. Patients may, therefore, be evaluated relatively higher while they are in the Domestic Section, for example, than while, during the assessment period, they are assigned to other tasks; and they may ultimately find employment in this field. The rehabilitation hospital has the advantage of injecting novelty into the helping professions, and of giving new meaning to the nurse-patient relationship.

∽§ OTHER PROGRAMS §∾

The rehabilitation hospital has been described in exacting detail as a new method of treatment. Similar programs have been established as experimental units in the United States and Canada for patients who have been ill for many years without becoming better (Fairweather, 1964; Colarelli and Siegel, 1966). An account of several programs, such as the Medfield and Weyburn projects, has been published by La Fave and his associates (La Fave *et al.*, 1965). We will compare these programs with St. Wulstan's as examples of an exciting movement.

There are striking characteristics at St. Wulstan's that are not duplicated in other hospitals. One difference is that St. Wulstan's is a self-contained and self-supporting institution, its only financial assistance being the Health Service appropriations common to all hospitals.[2] The program is paid for by the patients (from their earnings as workers) from the beginning of their stay; there is no period during which the patient is not paid for his work. Thus the rehabilitation hospital is a bona fide factory producing consumer goods and services and being itself a consumer and an added labor force to the community.

St. Wulstan's is a hospital in which functional diagnosis of the patients predominates, but it is not exclusively designed to cope with the schizophrenic patient, on whom so much attention has been focused. Epileptic patients with controlled seizures are among those who are outstandingly successful in finding employment. These patients are particularly known by the rehabilitation hospital staff for their ability to obtain a position but to lose it quickly through irritability and garrulous reaction to minor stress.

The rehabilitation hospital is an ongoing institution and is fundamentally different from projects that are designed, executed, and concluded after being evaluated by those involved in their creation. Many of these types have existed; they are usually located adjacent to, and sometimes as only an appendage to, the larger organizational structure. The Motivation Unit of the Downey Veterans Administration Hospital is an example of this type (Hoover, 1964). These programs are valuable for assessing patient potential and improving work skills, and much has been learned from their operation. Their longevity is dependent, however, upon factors existing in the larger hospital in the same way that the rehabilitation hospital's future is dependent upon a workable relationship with the parent hospitals.

Despite the fact that the rehabilitation hospital selects the best candidates from the parent hospitals' collective pool of patients (the entire aggregate of the twelve cachement areas), relations with

[2] The rehabilitation hospital's expenditure per patient is only slightly above that of other hospitals of comparable size, primarily because of the superior meals that are required for the working patient. The weekly maintenance cost is approximately £19 and the national average of all mental hospitals, which are nearly all much larger, is £13.

these institutions have been extremely good. This relationship may be a source of concern for other hospitals that are preparing to adopt this scheme, but it has not been a problem at St. Wulstan's, which fact is a commendation to the various parent hospital personnel. The staff of the rehabilitation hospital has the advantage of drawing upon an increasingly larger geographical area, and is bounded in this only by the distance from the patients' families and community ties. It is for this reason that the rehabilitation hospital staff sometimes may seek patients who have few family resources and who are favorably inclined toward relocation. These qualifications alone are not sufficient for admission, but may be important considerations as the field of operation is broadened.

The ideology of the rehabilitation hospital is not the same as that of an experimental program chiefly because its relation to the community is not the same. More than most programs, the rehabilitation hospital has a divided purpose: to serve both industry and patients, and the patients sometimes express the belief that they are working for the sound economy of the community and the country as a whole. The profit motive is not paramount, but the hospital/ factory is dependent upon local industry in a unique way. It is a cooperative enterprise between patients and staff with the expectation that the members of the current labor force will someday depart (an expectation not transmitted in equal terms toward the staff). In this way it is most unlike a factory. It is introduced into the community as a small, diversified industrial plant, but retains its name and identity as a hospital.

Unlike many hospitals, which rely to a considerable extent on volunteers spending their time talking with and assisting patients, the rehabilitation hospital has no active volunteer program or coordinator of volunteers. Lack of such contact with the community is felt to be a handicap by the staff. Since the patients are occupied throughout the day, volunteers, in order to spend time directly with the patients, would have to visit in the evenings or weekends or, in other words, at times in the week when these visits would often be inconvenient to the volunteers themselves. Many professional visitors, whose names are recorded in a guest book, come to the hospital.

Another feature of the rehabilitation hospital—which may

or may not be novel—is that potential staff members, after responding to a recruitment notice, are introduced to the hospital staff before they are finally selected from several people who have come for interviews. This procedure is voluntary for the staff candidates, even though it has become a tradition of the hospital. The candidates, both those from other hospitals and those within the staff who are applying for new positions, are feted informally at the Staff Club House the evening before their interviews. This meeting offers the members of the staff an opportunity to talk with these candidates about the rehabilitation hospital philosophy and to give them an insight into the work being done there. It also attests more strongly than anything else to the *esprit de corps* that exists among the staff members, and the lack of hierarchical concern in the thinking of the staff. This is perhaps most striking when the physician superintendent takes his turn according to the roster and serves at the bar.

Staff turnover is no greater at St. Wulstan's than at hospitals of comparable size; those staff members who leave do so for positions of more responsibility and higher salary.

In one important respect, the structure of the rehabilitation hospital compares favorably with that of other hospitals. Unlike other hospitals, St. Wulstan's does not attempt to transpose a static program onto a pre-existing structure, with the attendant strains that such a transposition creates; rather, its structure evolves to fit needs as they arise.

⪜ SMALL GROUPS ⪛

The conclusion reached by several investigators is that more attention must be paid to preparing the patient, in a practical way, to live outside the hospital. The small group was found to be the medium most effective for treatment (Fairweather, 1964). Small groups in the rehabilitation hospital are psychologically attached to centers of work, which constitute the most meaningful part of the patient's day. We do not imply that the presence of the group structure has any intrinsic meaning for the patients, and many staff members would doubt that it has. Nevertheless, the groups afford the patients and staff members an opportunity to discuss events that have taken place in the workshops and on weekend trips to the community, with an emphasis on the latter. Some staff members, like those of many hospitals, have no clear idea about the purpose of the groups and some become disillusioned by their experience in the groups. These feelings are properly channeled into the various staff meetings and Policy Committee.

In contrast to many other programs, the rehabilitation hospital knits the small-group concept into the total work program as a diversion in the middle of the working day. The small group includes the same staff members with whom the patients have been working that morning.

The description, in Fairweather's discussion, of the influence of social psychological processes upon patients working at structured tasks very nearly describes the organization of the rehabilitation hospital. Fairweather presents several generalizations that bear comparison with experiences at St. Wulstan's. Fairweather's points clarify the observations made in the course of the present study, and in the following conclusions the data from the two studies are in agreement.

1. We agree that patients should work alone without staff members in attendance, but only after a period of supervised work. The patients should feel that the staff members are in the area for consultation.

2. We agree that leadership is very important in establishing a group of patients who are effective in solving problems. Work in the rehabilitation hospital is not exactly "problem-solving activities"; however, the presence of staff members as problem-solving "role models" is essential.

3. We agree that meaningful rewards directly proportional to the patients' effort are essential, and this is the basis upon which the rehabilitation hospital operates.

4. We agree that the lack of autocratic relationships between staff members is mirrored in patient relationships. In our analysis of the staff questionnaire, however, we found agreement between staff members on several statements that indicate a need for direction and structure. Seventy-six per cent of the members agreed that

definite ranks among employees were essential so that all members knew their responsibilities. Seventy-two per cent disagreed with the statement that, within limits, in any mental hospital one professional worker can perform another's duties if the need arises. Regarding staff-patient relationships, 62 per cent agreed that the patients should be extended the privilege of choosing their own type of work. On the statement, "When it comes down to it, you have to push some patients to get things done," there was 84 per cent agreement, and no one strongly disagreed (see Appendix E).

We are not in agreement regarding the responsibility of the group for the individual patient's performance. The emphasis in the rehabilitation hospital is upon individual responsibility; this emphasis appears more in keeping with the policy of individual discharge of the patients. Regardless of whether the person is mentally disturbed or not, social alienation is a problem in society. We believe that the group experiences in the hospital aid in supporting these people ultimately to face the responsibilities of an individual separation from the hospital. This is achieved by not having the performance of their work group solely their responsibility if production lags.

Fairweather discusses the nature of the work given small groups in his program. No data are available regarding whether the patient's job should be a more encompassing task, such as managing a shop, or a more limited one, such as manufacturing a specific item. Both types of tasks occur in the rehabilitation hospital; whether a patient is given one type of task or the other depends on his condition. It is possible that the patient can perform a specific task, such as making out timecards for the workshops, and can be identified with the Clerical Section, in which this task is performed. Our observation indicates that patients in a smaller part of the hospital structure, such as the Clerical Section, identify with that section as a small group, whereas patients in the larger workshops identify with the task they are performing at the moment.

We agree that socially active-inactive heterogeneous groups of patients perform better than homogeneous ones. This conclusion was borne out by the study made by Sanders, MacDonald and Maynard and reported in the same book (Fairweather, 1964). It was found in the rehabilitation hospital that some patients in Gold

Unit were socially retarded, but were earning at the same level as the more socially out-going ones. It is fair to say that no single unit in the hospital was composed only of inactive patients, so a direct comparison on this variable could not be made. Three statements on the work reports pertain to the person's seeking out more work, and talking with staff members and other patients. We found that these activities were related to earnings. The work report, however, does not reflect an aspect of social activity highly important for rehabilitation, that is, making unsupervised journeys into the community, and following up employment possibilities.[3] These variables do not appear to be related to performance on the job.

⋖§ SUMMARY §⋗

Most rehabilitation programs have some features that could relieve the psychological and physical plight of the poor.

Believing that by comparing programs we can best point out the distinguishing features of the rehabilitation hospital, we have commented that the program at St. Wulstan's is more fluid in accepting all types of chronically unemployed, sick or well, young and old, than other programs are. The rehabilitation hospital is more self-supporting and is staffed in such a way that it continues after a period of evaluation. We have found that our observations are in agreement with many of the conclusions made by other investigators who have studied the same types of patients in small groups in similar settings.

Let us continue with the studies and, more importantly, the conclusions to which we made reference under point number four in this chapter.

---

[3] Efforts are being made to perfect the Work Report along this line by members of the hospital nursing staff and the physician superintendent.

 *FIVE*

The Evaluation Process

Although research is not the primary focus of this book, it is important for the evaluative processes intrinsic to effective rehabilitation programs. To recognize the limitations of these evaluative processes is equally important. These limitations are often intrinsic to the programs themselves. Some limitations oc-

cur in the mere starting of a program. Kandel and Williams (1964), for example, describe the resistance some investigators encountered in establishing a control group where some patients are deprived of the treatment condition. Eysenck (1961) has written succinctly on this subject and pointed out that until a treatment is found to be beneficial no real argument of deprivation is valid. Contamination from changes in the control group is also a problem. We recognized that the mere fact of singling out a patient to be a member of a control group may function to produce unpredictable changes in his condition.

Another problem in this evaluation was found in the search for an uncontaminated control group of patients. The members of the control group for these studies were patients who had been selected for admission to the rehabilitation hospital but who had not yet been admitted. These patients were found either to be more involved with an ultimate placement with their families, or to be less positive in their attitude toward rehabilitation, than those who were admitted. In other instances, the patients in this potential control group

65

had subsequently been placed in rehabilitation programs in the parent hospital.

To further complicate the search for a control group, we found no "rehabilitation-free" hospital in the same geographical area, nor any that was of similar size to St. Wulstan's so that an institutional control was not possible. We therefore decided to use, wherever possible, tests among patients in the rehabilitation hospital itself, using length-of-time-in-the-environment as the dependent variable. In these studies, one year was designated as the critical period between assessments. The two exceptions to this design were (1) the investigation of the types of re-education instruction where a control group within the hospital was permitted in the test-retest design, and (2) a retest of patients in some aspects of the self-image study.

❧ FACTORS AFFECTING ACHIEVEMENT ❧

Knowledge of the demographic variables that lead to a patient's rehabilitation is important for practical as well as for theoretical reasons. The practical value of isolating those factors in the patient's social history that increase his chances of completing the program is obvious where financial considerations are concerned.[1] An investigation of these factors will contribute to our understanding of chronic illness as it determines what is important to rehabilitating the patient. It will also provide some bases for predicting the success of a rehabilitation program with a group of normal people who show the same demographic characteristics and who require similar vocational assistance.

Social Class

We will first consider social class as a factor. In the broadest

---

[1] In the study cited earlier and reported by Dr. Morgan (Morgan et al., 1965), attention was paid to the descriptive variables of the hospital ward from which the patients were admitted to the rehabilitation hospital—such variables as restrictiveness, age, occupation, and other factors pertaining directly to the patient. We will turn our attention to further factors which have been shown to be related to remission and types of treatment.

of perspectives, the work of Hollingshead and Redlich (1958) and Myers and Roberts (1959) has demonstrated that social class is one determinant in the traditional forms of treatment of the mentally disturbed. Their findings have shown a close relationship between social class and (1) treatment or absence of treatment, (2) types of psychiatric disorders, (3) types of treatment offered, and (4) the development of illness.

Although these findings resulted from research in America, there is little reason to believe that the same class structure does not exist in the British population that was studied in this evaluation. Differential treatment of patients from different social classes is undoubtedly more apparent immediately following their first episode of illness; however, the factor of social class is not among the criteria for transfer to the rehabilitation hospital. We readily recognize that, among the very wealthy, even the most chronic patients can afford long-term care in private hospitals and sanatoria; for this reason, these patients are not represented in the group studied here.

Still, it is the premise of this study that intraclass differences existing in the patients' histories are important in their differential rehabilitation advancement.

Myers and Roberts found that the inability to achieve success was a significant factor in the frustration experienced by the patients in the middle class, or Class III. In Class V, or lower class, the finding pertinent to rehabilitation was that patients from this class experienced lifelong economic insecurity and feelings of exploitation. This is especially relevant to the poverty victim, who is, by definition, from the lower classes.

The rehabilitation hospital serves the needs of the frustrated patient from both of these classes, but in different ways. The Class III patient is afforded recognition of a job well done in the frequent reviews of his work and is given tasks that he can perform in the program. The Class V patient is given an opportunity for employment without exploitation and with financial security, not only in the hospital but afterwards. It is logical to assume, therefore, that patients from both classes would successfully work through the program.

One factor that is possibly class-linked is the willingness or ability of the patient's parents and siblings to accommodate him after discharge. The patient from a lower class may be a greater financial burden on his family than a patient from a higher class family would. It is assumed that family intentions would be a specious factor in the study of who benefits from such a hospital for two reasons: (1) the long-term patient is ordinarily psychologically abandoned long before admission to the rehabilitation hospital, and (2) this variable is not taken into consideration when review committees consider the patient for transfer to another unit. Admission to the rehabilitation hospital occasionally reawakens family interest in the patient for, at least, a brief period. In some cases, the family reacts negatively, particularly when the hospital is unable to inform the members of the family (who often have not visited the patient in the parent hospital for years) of the discharge to the rehabilitation hospital.

An exception to our premise may be occupation as a class variable. Occupation involves the rural-urban characteristic of the patient. It has been shown that, among male patients, a rural background enhances the possibility of remaining out of the hospital in at least one subculture studied (Query and Query, 1964). Apart from this, the industrial nature of the work in the hospital/factory suggests that patients with an urban background are more likely to complete the program, particularly if they worked in factory settings before hospitalization occurred. Agricultural or farm laborers are less likely to complete the program, being more non-achievers than achievers.[2]

As described in Chapter 3, Gold Unit most nearly approximates working conditions in the open market, that is, a forty-hour work week, unsupervised work, and unsupervised night living conditions in the unit. All patients working in this unit were defined as "achievers" in this study for purposes of comparison. In the Blue

---

[2] Some patients have several occupational experiences in their histories. In these cases notation is made of the longest job held for the purposes of comparison. In many cases, the "job" the patient would refer to upon inquiry would be the assignment he had in the parent hospital. This is quite a natural thing for the long-term and unemployed patient to say. These "jobs" were disregarded in the analysis.

Unit, few of these conditions prevail; the environment is in sharp contrast to the environment in Gold Unit. The patients there are defined as non-achievers or at least as non-achievers at this time.

Environmental Factors

In planning the study of the characteristics that marked the people who did well in the program, we compared the patients in one unit with those in another unit along specific dimensions we reasoned to be important. The factors leading to achievement in a hospital/factory can be divided into: (1) those characteristics that identify the patient upon admission, which can be manipulated in terms of criteria for admission, and (2) those that accrue to the patient in the course of his rehabilitation.

We considered several characteristics, other than those already cited, in the first category of factors. The number of years spent in the parent hospital was an example. The entire program was founded on the notion that the chronic patient can be rehabilitated. It was assumed, however, that within the range of hospitalization represented, the longer the patient had been hospitalized, the less he was likely to achieve. We also predicted that the achieving patients would have spent fewer years in the parent hospital than the non-achievers.

Age

We turn next to the age of the patient at the time his rehabilitation was begun. This factor seemed important for both physical and psychological reasons. The older patient usually had been given less preparation while he was at the parent hospital and consequently showed accompanying physical decline. This patient usually had fewer outside interests and was less likely to be stimulated by the staff. Achievers, therefore, were those patients who were younger at the time of their admission to the parent hospital.

However, younger patients are often in an acute phase of illness, or perhaps in a highly confused state after an acute episode, and are less approachable. They are, in the jargon, "burned out," or completely affectless and unresponsive. It is this type of patient that is thought to be more amenable to rehabilitation. So, although younger patients are better achievers, they seem to require a period of chronicity before a fresh start can bring positive results.

Psychosurgery

Some factors posited to enhance achievement in the workshop may develop in the hospital itself, and be related to the factors mentioned above. As an example of this, age at which rehabilitation began may be related directly to number of days in the clinic: the older the patient, the less acute his psychosis, and the fewer days spent in the clinic. The same patient may be off the job and treated for brief periods for physical problems due to aging.

We might expect the achievers to have spent significantly fewer days in the clinic within the same period of time than non-achievers. The number of weeks each patient spent in the clinic was found by investigating the wage reports and other notations of the patients' progress in the case-papers.

It is reasonable to assume also that psychosurgery is in itself a debilitating factor for industrial work, particularly in some phases of industrial workshop activities. Psychosurgery would be especially important if the staff were considering for placement, in the vicinity of industrial machinery, patients who had a history of seizures. This factor may not be recognized by staff in review committee decisions when they place non-seizure patients in unsupervised workshop activities. We selected for analysis, therefore, the records of patients who had no known seizures. We expected to find fewer lobotomized patients (without seizures) among the achievers than among the non-achievers, because their postoperative behavior, even without overt seizures, would very likely preclude their finding employment —even within the rehabilitation hospital—on the types of jigs and mechanical devices used in industrial workshops.

The factor of marriage is suggestive of a "good" prognosis. We tested the extent to which marriage determined achievement in the hospital.

Incentive

Incentive in the rehabilitation hospital is the security and recognition of the workshop. These were powerful incentives for

Class III and Class V patients. We anticipated that this incentive would be reflected in two ways: (1) a higher initial wage at the beginning of their tenure in the program, and (2) better work report scores. The achieving patients would not only be in an advanced unit, but their work records would show these trends when compared with those of the non-achievers.

We stated in the description of the units in Chapter 3 that patients considered as not achieving are given the routine contracts on which to work. Although no assumptions can be formulated regarding the variety of work given the patients and their level of achievement, one would expect that the achievers would have a greater variety of tasks given to them. This variety would produce greater flexibility in their training and would certainly place them in a better position for employment.

We must mention again that these factors are not to be considered in isolation. Another example will suffice: the higher initial wage for the achievers before the ceiling is reached might be related to their marital status. The married patient would have a greater incentive to raise the level of his earnings. This could be found by a test of association (see Appendix A for this procedure) between these two factors, irrespective of whether the patient is in the unit defined as containing achieving patients or in the comparison unit. We checked the records of the patients in the contrasting units and made appropriate statistical tests. (These tests are described in Appendix A.)

Results

In evaluating the results of these tests, we found a few clearcut conclusions from isolatable factors; but most of the characteristics, such as urban or rural, were either interrelated or not significant. Among the main factors there were six that were significant, five that showed predicted trends but were not statistically significant, and three that were not significant (see Table A-1 in Appendix A). One of the more clearcut results was unexpected. We found that the siblings of achievers (when they had siblings) were unwilling to accommodate them after discharge. There was no difference regarding parents and wives on this variable. This result quite possibly reflects an independence from siblings which is prognostically favorable in terms of such a work program as this one.

We found some specific factors are significant and independent of other factors. For example, separating the achievers from the non-achievers according to social classes are found in both units. A less obvious finding was that the patient's age is no problem for his completing the work in the hospital/factory and attaining achievement status by working in the final phase of the program. In fact, the older person holds an advantage in this regard, provided he does not suffer from schizophrenia. We also use the male pronoun advisedly because we found that a thinking disorder of the depth of schizophrenia disables women more profoundly than men in terms of their achieving the purposes of the program.

We reasoned that the responsibilities of marriage would increase the married man's motivation to do well financially and that he would select more remunerative jobs or at least earn more in his stay. This assumption, when incentive is measured by actual earnings, is not borne out. Regardless of the unit, single men earn only slightly less than the married ones.

We chose two ways of measuring chronicity among several possibilities: length of time in the parent hospital and age when rehabilitation began. We found that length of time was not a significant factor and, contrariwise, the older the person at the beginning of rehabilitation, the greater the chances of achievement. We found support for the "chronicity hypothesis" from this means of measurement. It should be noted, however, that both groups' averages were within the forty-to-fifty age bracket.

Achievement was no more characteristic of the urban persons than of persons from rural backgrounds. Although a trend was noted, radical operations such as psychosurgery did not interfere with achievement, nor did other types of operations that were occasionally performed.

The non-achievers spent longer time and there were more of them in the clinic setting (described in Chapter 3). This suggests more that the clinic is valuable than that it is unnecessary, because the fact remains that achievers were occasionally admitted to the clinic.

It was generally assumed that the work report was valuable as a means of measuring a type of achievement. Although the work report scores reflected actual earnings, we had a problem in using them to gauge improvement. The ultimate achievers earned such "good" scores at the outset of their work that most of the rated improvement went to the non-achievers by default. Other explanations of this result, such as the differences in emphasis among the various unit staff personnel, are possible.

The work report scores showing improvement among both non-achievers and achievers must be evaluated even more closely because the person's sex was a significant factor. Not only did schizophrenic men perform better than schizophrenic women, but men, more than women, showed greater rated improvement among the less achieving group of patients as well as among schizophrenics.

We found that the achieving patients' overall experiences included a variety of tasks. This variety may be one factor for achievement after other important factors have been considered.

The investigation summarized above was simply a comparison between two selected units, using all the patients assigned to those units. From the nature of the units we defined these patients as achievers or non-achievers. In the balance of the studies in this evaluation we utilized tests, questionnaires, and other devices of measurement that require some explanation. In some cases, we constructed the instruments; in others, we used instruments for psychological measurement that already existed. In a few instances, we had to adapt these instruments to our British population. The matter of phraseology and idioms was taken up with the members of the staff. The details of these procedures can be found in the appropriate appendices: Appendix A for the foregoing study, Appendices B and E for the studies that remain for us to discuss in this chapter, and Appendix G for the study set apart for review in Chapter 6.

Progress in the rehabilitation hospital depends only partly on such measures as work scores. Change in personality characteristics is another important aspect of progress, particularly where group participation on a project is concerned.

✑ EFFECTS OF THE HOSPITAL ON PATIENTS ⧫

The purpose of this study was to determine, first, what characteristics of patients who were placed in open employment were valued by the staff according to the ideology of the rehabilitation hospital, and second, to determine whether the role model concept in social role theory was valid for determining progress in a rehabilitation program of this kind. In order to find measurable characteristics, we asked staff members to select adjectives for mental patients as attributes they believed were important in securing employment and holding a job for at least one year. They were to rely on their experience in the rehabilitation hospital in formulating their replies. They were later to rate the patients on these characteristics. (We assume that these attributes are equally valuable for the poverty victim.) On this basis, we formulated a list of adjectives after rejecting some ambiguities and duplications. One ambiguity escaped our attention; it is discussed below, under "Self-image and Trait Analysis." A few adjectives, such as those with a psychosexual connotation, were chosen by the examiner specifically to determine the extent of change. Adjectives were included, for example, that were used to test work perseverance and socially approved self-images. The list of these adjectives, called traits, is found in Appendix C.

We were aware of the possibility of projection on the part of the staff in rating the patient (Campbell et al., 1964), but the validity of the ratings was not the main concern. Our main concern was establishing whether our adjective checklist could measure self-image learning through social interaction and whether self-image learning occurred as predicted in a hospital of this kind. Learning new roles with an accompanying self-image shift toward an institution's ideological norm is a complex process, involving reference group affiliation and social expectation. We gave several tests to the same subjects to measure their expectations of being able, after their discharge, to do various common tasks. This technique involved several sortings of the same tasks from different frames of reference.

We had reason to believe that basic personality dimensions—such as being essentially socially retiring or outgoing—would be relatively unaffected by the hospital program coming, as it did, in adulthood. We predicted that although basic personality remained unchanged, a person would change his image of himself more on some traits than on others, and that most self-images would alter to some extent. An example of a self-image trait characteristic of the unemployable as well as of the mental patient is the feeling of dependency, which is highly susceptible to change. We predicted that reliance on role models (the term we adopted for the staff members who worked with these people) in the rehabilitation hospital environment would inculcate a feeling of dependency, out of which would grow a feeling of self-assurance. The conclusions are reported under two broad headings, the first dealing with patient self-images, and the second, with the relationship between patients' self-images and their role model images. In order to ascertain the rise and fall of these changes, we constructed a design for an experiment that used three samples of the patient population, rather than two— that is, *short-stay, medium-stay,* and *long-stay* groups. We would, therefore, predict a high level of self-image independence among the short-stay group, because no dependency relationship to a role model would have been formed in the parent hospital; a trend toward dependency among the medium-stay group, stemming from the effect of the role models and the patient's dependency on them; and a trend toward greater independence among the long-stay group. We checked our results from this procedure; that is, we assessed three groups by following up our first assessment of the short-stay group nine months later. This check was only partly successful, as some of the short-stay patients were discharged or returned to the parent hospital before the second assessment.

The effect of the program suggests other predictions: there will be predictable self-image changes, consistent with the length of stay, in the direction of the views held by staff members regarding adequate prerequisites for rehabilitation. These changes will affect the sex identification, the image of personal worth, dependency or independence, anxiety level, personal feelings of attraction, interpersonal feelings (being easily hurt or highly sensitive to criticism), pessimism or optimism, confidence, and general activity level.

We assumed that adequate role models are necessary for industrial rehabilitation and learning in a social context to take place. There will be a realistic change in the self-image of the person as he approaches the role model's evaluation of him. The person whose image of himself approximates that of the staff member with whom he works will be among the achievers in the advanced units of the hospital. The person who is still in the period of finding an adequate role model, or who is less advanced, will be in the medium-stay group. Patients who have only recently entered the rehabilitation environment will have little congruence between their self-images and those of the role models. As noted at the beginning of the chapter no control group (without role models) was possible in a hospital of the same type as this one, so that this ideal control was not forthcoming.

In order to lend realism to the rating scheme, *hard-working* was one of the traits chosen. This trait is highly acceptable socially and very relevant to the rehabilitation situation.[3]

Our assumption of role relationships suggested a second prediction: there will be little congruence, that is, similarity, between the self-image and role model's image of the patient in the short-stay group; there will be greater congruence in the medium-stay group; and greatest congruence will occur among the long-stay and achieving group. The dependent variable again is the length of time in the hospital.

Can these results be equally and more cogently explained by the role model's increased knowledge of and familiarity with the patient? So that this factor might be minimized, two members of the staff for each group were used as raters, both of whom knew the patients, but one of whom in each group had been in the rehabilitation hospital as a staff member for a short time. In some cases, the patients who were placed in the same groups as subjects according to length of stay worked in different units and were evaluated by different staff members. It was not possible to control the sex of the role models, that is, to have both male, or both female, or one male

---

[3] Note should be taken of the fact that the ratings were not in any way comparable to the work reports routinely made on the patients. The work reports deal with a series of continua and patterns of behavior in the work situation.

and one female in each group. All role models were assigned to the workshop units, as were the patients they rated.

As a direct way of measuring the role model concept, each patient was first asked: "To whom would you go for the best advice and help on your job in the hospital?" Only those patients who had been in the hospital the prescribed length of time to be included in one of the groups, who had been matched for age and length of hospitalization in the parent hospital, who met the intellectual criterion, and who noted one of the same staff members on their units in response to this question, were retained in the groups.

To recapitulate, in the course of this particular study we asked patients to re-evaluate themselves on the traits after nine months had elapsed as a check on the results obtained from dividing the patients into three groups according to length of stay. Members of the short-stay group re-evaluated themselves with the same instrument.

Results

A number of our initial expectations were not substantiated. Personality *does* change within the framework of the rehabilitation environment as it was measured by the personality test that we chose (for description of this test see Appendix B). The change is different between men and women patients.

The results pertaining to the self-images are reviewed below, and occasional serendipitous findings that the data yielded are included.

1. Increased anxiety characterized the medium-stay patient's self-image as he experienced greater achievement. This anxiety diminished by the time long-term status had been acquired.

2. The patients became more optimistic, more confident, had a feeling of being better liked, and less a feeling of being easily hurt in their interpersonal relationships.

3. There was an inconclusive trend toward greater masculinity as a self-image among long-stay men, and greater femininity among women, but this characteristic was dependent upon assignment and work experience in the hospital program. Despite minimal

change in areas closely related to the work role, the effect of the environment radiated to this area, which is obviously related to experiences other than work.

4. There was evidence that sexual role differentiation occurred with stay in the hospital. Although some men rated themselves more masculine, the personality inventory test data showed increased femininity on the scale among men. Rated images and scale scores were not always identical.

5. Stay in the rehabilitation hospital also affected change in the following areas: less absent-mindedness, greater self-evaluated intelligence, less strength and neatness, and less moodiness, which, in turn, may be clinically related to the first of the traits listed here. This suggested to us that the patients may grow more aware of events (less absent-minded) and less caught up in rumination over events they think might occur.

6. Feelings of both independence and dependency tended toward the predicted results: that there would be little significant change. As the patients remained in the hospital, they rated themselves more independent and less dependent. We do not pretend that the ratings resulted from operationally unquestionable tests; they probably are not as valid as measures employing behavioral categories, such as avoider-approacher classifications, projective fantasy measures, or standard situation tests. All of these types of measures were used in one piece of research by Goldman (1965). Tests such as these, however, fail to measure our main concern, that is, how dependent the person construes himself to be. It is still possible that, as more discriminating measures become available, the tendencies we have found will have become confirmations with further research.

7. *Hard-working* was a positive trait shared by all patients in all groups, and *sick* was a shared negative trait. There was a tendency for *slow* and *valuable,* particularly *slow,* to be confirmed as changing with stay in the hospital. Both were relatively high among the medium-stay subjects.

In summary, six critical trait changes were statistically significant, seven were found to change in the predicted direction but not significant, and five showed scarcely any change whatsoever.

The large number of self-image ratings that yielded data in the predicted directions would have produced an impressive collection of environmental effects if significance had been consistently found. It is likely that these ratings show the least impact of the rehabilitation hospital environment. We conclude that effects have been demonstrated and that, with further elaboration and additional subjects in the groups, even more definitive results can be obtained. This conclusion is bolstered by the large differences found in the test-retest of patients on the personality test. The fact remains that our findings concerning the changes that were due exclusively to role models are still tenuous without a control hospital. It would be virtually impossible to locate a hospital with the same milieu, where, at the same time, patients worked without staff member direction.

Self-image and Trait Analysis

An analysis of how the staff evaluates the patients and how the patients evaluate themselves clarifies the effect of such a hospital on the people who live in it. The analysis in this example shows that congruence, or agreement between raters and rated, is irregular but meaningful when we consider the organizational structure of the hospital/factory.

The image traits themselves served as a means of determining what traits were most congruent in terms of agreement between the role models. We first determined upon which traits the staff members agreed regardless of how the patients marked themselves. These data only indicate the traits that role models agreed upon when rating the patients. From highest in agreement, the following traits are listed in descending order: [4]

Strong
{ Broad-minded
{ Hard-working
Neat
Slow

[4] The brackets throughout indicate the same frequency of congruence or agreement regardless whether staff members rate patients and patients rate themselves or whether there is agreement *between* staff members rating patients as in the above.

{ Optimistic
  Confident
  Dependent
  Happy
  Clean
  Sick

Agreement seemed to be achieved on more positive traits and socially valued concepts, such as the first four, and those directly concerned with the work and appearance of the patients at the rehabilitation hospital.

Those traits where disagreement was characteristic were more negative, or less concerned with the work of the hospital. Many were of the same frequency of agreement. These are listed from the lowest in ascending order:

Stubborn
{ Suspicious
  Religious
  Obedient
  Angry
  Conceited
  Loud
{ Absent-minded
  Brave
  Greedy
  Moody
  Scheming

Next, the same data are tabulated in terms of agreement between the patient's self-image and the role models' opinions, or the staff-patient congruence. From highest in descending order we find:

Broad-minded
{ Intelligent
  Strong
  Neat
  Anxious
{ Conceited
  Dependent
  Happy

{ Masculine
Optimistic
Hard-working

Some discrepancies are evident. *Hard-working,* for example, showed more agreement between role models than between patients and role models. *Broad-minded, neat,* and *strong* were traits about which everyone seemed to agree. *Conceited, masculine,* and *anxious* were traits on which the patients were more in accord with one of the two role models than the role models were with each other.

We reversed the listing and found those traits that were best agreed upon by the staff members were those that the staff members did not agree upon when they rated the patients.

Ranking these data from the lowest in ascending order, we find the following arrangement:

Sick
Stubborn
Suspicious
{ Absent-minded
Moody
{ Obedient
Religious
Active
{ Critical
Scheming

Important in this list is the first trait, *sick,* which had very little congruence, but was relatively high between role models as a trait about which they agreed. This finding suggests either that the patients did not have the same definition, that is, mental sickness (and there is reason to believe that some of the role models did not share a common definition) or that the patients did not agree with their role models on their state of health, regardless of the definition used as a reference. The latter is considered to be more valid when we check the direction of the *lack* of congruence and find that the patient, regardless of time in the rehabilitation hospital, places himself as "about average" rather than toward the position the role model had assigned him. This is not unusual among chronic patients, and particularly among those who are in a rehabilitation milieu.

The data pertaining to staff and patient agreement were also analyzed in terms of change between short-stay, medium-stay, and long-stay grouping. The following traits showed an *increase of agreement* over time. The traits are listed according to increase, with the greatest increases at the beginning, in descending order:

Angry
Anxious
Greedy
Religious
Stubborn
Suspicious

Does this result mean that the patients are viewed and view themselves as becoming more angry as they remain in the hospital? When we analyzed the direction, we found that there was a slight increase in the number of patients *not* showing the self-image of being angry over time, with a similar increase in staff agreement. There was a non-significant decrease in this trait being marked affirmatively among those patients who performed the ratings a second time. We interpret these results as indicating that the rehabilitation hospital environment has the effect of reducing anger, or the feeling of being an angry person. This finding is important when generalized to the person who is plagued by poverty in an affluent social system and who may feel anger in this situation.

There was found a *decrease* in patients having the self-image of *cleanliness* and *neatness* with staff agreement over time. This result suggests a growing feeling of being untidy among the patients, with staff concurrence.

There was no trait congruent between patients and staff that showed a decrease over time irrespective of direction. Two traits were the same throughout the groups: *broad-minded* and *optimistic*. Both of these traits showed relatively high agreement.

The results of this section show that self-image becomes more congruent with role model perception through the first two and a half years of patients' stay in the hospital. Thereafter, there is a group of patients where greater congruence is not indicated and our prediction is borne out with these limitations. The role models agree on traits having more practical application to the work of the rehabilitation hospital. *Anxiousness,* as a self-image in which there was particular theoretical interest, is not a shared image trait between role models, but the patients accurately agree on the trait as a self-image and the image tends to increase and then decrease with the pressure of the work. This result is in accordance with the increasing demands on the patient and the accommodation the patients make to these demands. We found that the patients consistently marked themselves either as *sick* or as *average*. Taking only the extremes and *average* markings on this self-image, it was found that, out of the fifty-one patients represented, twenty patients marked themselves as *not sick,* twenty-six, *about average,* and only nine as *sick*. Seventeen of the seventy-two patients were more cautious in their estimates and marked themselves as *moderately not sick,* and only one considered himself *moderately sick*.

Among a small group of patients we found that patients whose evaluations of themselves were similar to the role models' evaluations stayed on their jobs longer after rehabilitation. As stated earlier, this increase in common evaluation exists up to two and a half years while the patient remains in the program.

This experiment showed that one of the effects of the milieu we are studying is to produce among patients less *unrealistic* expectations of themselves in the future. It does not necessarily produce more *realistic* ones. This conclusion is based on the finding that when given the opportunity to mark realistic and unrealistic items, the patients who were in the hospital longer marked fewer unrealistic items but failed to substitute for these items an increased number of realistic ones in terms of their future. Furthermore, there was a tendency for the number of future expectations, regardless of their being realistic or not, to decrease with stay in the hospital. The patient becomes more firm in his general role, as shown by the decrease in "don't know" responses. However, there are no data to show that these changes do not occur in the usual hospital setting. As to reference group theory, when the patients rather than their responses are taken as a point of reference, we find a demonstrable change

toward the patients viewing themselves as members of the rehabilitation hospital and away from viewing themselves as mental patients. There is a category of patients who come to the rehabilitation
hospital feeling that, as mental patients, little can be expected of
them, but who feel that, if they are considered only as people, and
not as mental patients, much more can be expected of them both
now and in the future. We conjectured that this feeling was linked
to a particular hospital milieu and we found evidence for this possibility. The majority of newcomers to the hospital show affiliation
with the general mental patient; these patients expect little of themselves, both now and in the future.

Even these patients change, however, both in their self-
images and in their personality tendencies, the greatest decrease for
both men and women being in the dimension of self-control. The
data showing personality change were gathered from a select sample
of the more intelligent patients and such change at the more basic
level may be restricted to these patients.

The areas in which self-image changes were found were all
socially approved areas. The patients conformed also to the rating
behavior that characterizes normal people in ascribing socially approved traits to themselves and not ascribing socially disapproved
traits to themselves. These results are consistent with another finding
in this study, that is, that patients are able to distinguish between
realistic and unrealistic future goals, and to delimit the number of
future expectations generally. It is almost as though the patient in
the rehabilitation hospital is saying, "I know myself and what lies
ahead a little better. I will not expect too much and endanger my
newly found optimism and confidence."

๙ EFFECTS OF THE HOSPITAL ON STAFF ๖

The purpose of this part of our research into the workings of
the rehabilitation hospital was to explore the attitudes prevalent
among the staff members, and how these attitudes affected the activities of these staff members in performing their jobs. It is reasonable to predict that the unique composition of the hospital affects

the staff members' attitudes. The direction of change that these attitudes take was investigated with a small number of the staff.

Our topic is introduced by an interesting observation concerning the twenty-two male and three female members of the nursing staff who were chosen as role models. We obtained information about these people and their principal previous occupations. They were all qualified psychiatric nurses, but a surprising number had experience in other fields. Ten of the twenty-five had always been nurses as well as could be determined, and one (male) had a father in this profession. Many others had come into nursing in their late twenties, after both training and experience in a variety of other occupations: two had been engineers, three had been musicians and one of these had also been a physical training instructor, three had been laborers, and one each, an actor, a member of the building trades, a navy career man, a typist, a member of the garment trade, a bus conductor, and an electrician. This variety of backgrounds outside nursing might account for two other observations: (1) the easy adaptability of these nurses to the factory conditions of the rehabilitation hospital, and (2) the hesitancy some displayed in placing full production pressure on the patients because, in some cases, it was this very pressure that prompted their own change of career. This remark does not mean to imply that a complete lack of pressure prevailed in the rehabilitation hospital, but only that some nurses were loathe to convey the effects of the pressure onto their charges. Such was the professional nature of many of the people who served as role models. In many conversations, however, these people gave a definite impression of compassionate interest rather than one of purely business interests.

In the programs designed to alleviate poverty many of the training personnel, like these nurses, come from other fields. Their motivation may or may not be more service-oriented than that of the nurses described here, but the fact that they have backgrounds in other areas of work makes them similar in this way to the nurses, and therefore suggests that we can generalize our findings to these training personnel.

Another effect more directly related to the role model concept was suggested by the variety of backgrounds found in these nurses' careers. Were these people, we might question, more motivated toward furthering their professional status, which some of them only recently attained? (We can call this motivation "profession orientation.") Or did the industrial past of some of them, along with the fundamental work milieu of the rehabilitation hospital, dictate more a "production orientation"?

We tested these orientations in two ways: (1) by constructing an inventory of agree, disagree, or neutral reaction to statements for each orientation, and (2) by asking the staff members what course of action they would take in actual situations presumably testing these orientations when one was pitted against another. Our exact procedure along with the statistical results and different ways of looking at the data are contained in Appendix E. This chapter contains some percentages of categories of response on critical statements. It is sufficient to comment here that we developed the scale through recognized procedures and made some adjustments according to its length. We also checked the validity of this scale by what we called "situational tests." We administered a third scale, designed to measure attitudes toward the mentally ill, which was developed elsewhere, and we compared our results with hospitals from which data were available. We separated our data into staffs of the various units—those who had direct relationship with the patients and those who did not, those who wore uniforms and those who did not, and other separations—to make our analysis more meaningful. Many of these results are tangential to our major conclusions and are not summarized here. Before reporting the conclusions we will consider our basic rationale.

One's background determines to some degree one's orientation. The last question regarding an exclusively production orientation is particularly relevant for those members of the staff who were involved in maintaining deadlines. One would expect that a patient orientation would be more characteristic of the thinking of nurses who had had little other experience outside this profession. All three orientations were of interest in how they were affected by and/or set the pattern of the official hospital ideology. We were therefore interested to find whether one orientation was associated with attitudes toward patient care, such as custodialism.

A *post hoc* study of the influence of attitudes on estimation of work performance does not substitute for a controlled study of these variables. It gives us insight, however, into how attitudes might influence a patient's progress and the progress of any other person through the rehabilitation program. A role model's acute interest in the management of his unit toward raising production (a high production orientation) might produce a halo effect, resulting in his giving some patients a better work report score (a low score), which would, in turn, be taken into consideration for promoting patients into more responsibility in another unit. The same constellation of factors might affect the role model's judgment to the extent that he would not encourage promotion of those patients who contributed to the high production of the unit. In the rehabilitation hospital, such variables as space accommodations, behavior reports, and the opinions of other members of the staff affect these decisions, so that the effects of the attitude of any single person are greatly reduced.

Results

We found that the role models, as typified by the staff members in the units, are oriented in actual situations toward professional advancement. There are conspicuous exceptions to this generalization where task pressures are very keenly felt in the unit. Profession orientation is inextricably linked with a strong patient orientation, and the staff member sees training in his field as a means of helping patients and achieving greater insight into their behavior. The orientations of the staff members follow a path from profession through production to profession orientation. Throughout this path, a high level of interest in the patient is steadily maintained from all members of the staff.

The wisdom of an attempt to validate the results on the orientation scales with the situational tests was demonstrated, and we found differing results. We found a high proportion of patient orientation among the staff members on the scales. This result was mitigated on the situational tests by the showing of a high orientation toward professional advancement.

The situations were not of similar weight and differed markedly in the plausibility of the circumstances they described, but we can conclude that, when professional advancement (aside from the rehabilitation hospital) and the patients' interests are in conflict, the staff will not involve themselves in a dependent fashion with the patients. This would probably be equally true if such a program were introduced to alleviate the psychological effects of poverty.

Production was not emphasized in the chronic unit, where the patients required more supervision. Taking the work report scores as examples of statements about patients that might be influenced by staff attitudes, little relationship was found to exist among the variables. In two units, however, we found particularly high orientations in one unit toward production and, in the other unit, toward patients. The patient orientation was related to low or more favorable work scores. This relation suggests that rating the concrete behavior of patients may be determined by more global, or more encompassing, staff attitudes.

The data show a change in the staff member's attitude toward patients and in his general orientation. After a period of months in the rehabilitation hospital milieu, the staff member becomes more confirmed in his beliefs, showing an increase in all orientations, but most particularly in his orientation toward the work of the hospital. The "neutral" categories dropped, for example, from 30 per cent to 14 per cent in the retest with the questionnaire.

An increase in custodialism, as measured by the scale we chose, occurs but is readily explained by the ideology that staff members learn in the rehabilitation hospital. A production orientation was the only one found to be related to custodialism. The ideology is one of temporary custody of the patient, with a concentration of work and structured re-education. If this is what is meant by "custodialism," the environment of the rehabilitation hospital engenders this feeling.

An evaluation of any institution requires a summary statement about how people who work there feel about their jobs and those with whom they work. Controversy and agreement often typify the working conditions of such an institution, and this is no less true for the hospital/factory as we know it. For this evaluation, a questionnaire was given. Seven of the questionnaire statements were found to be controversial—that is, these seven items had less than 30 per cent under any one response category. There were five that indicated considerable communality of opinion—that is, these five items had 60 per cent or greater agreement in any category. These conclusions were based on all the data, not only on the nurses' responses.

Controversial and Communality Items

Analyzing the controversial items, we concluded that: (1) There was a tendency to agree that staff members from particular sections of the rehabilitation hospital should eat together and so facilitate communication. The smallness of the hospital might indicate otherwise. (2) Some thought that there were too many formal meetings in the rehabilitation hospital. Both topics were especially controversial, showing a wide variety of opinion. (3) Whether it is the presence of the staff, such as performing role models, or the work itself that benefits patients is a question to which there was little agreement. (4) Some staff members felt that they had changed in their attitude toward patients since working with them, and some did not believe so. (5) There was disagreement about recommending their profession or type of work to a young person, partly because the sex of the young person was not specified in the statement. The lack of agreement here undoubtedly tapped some job dissatisfaction, or a feeling that because an older person might handle their job better, they would not recommend it to a young person.

In analyzing the communality items, we concluded that: (1) All staff members, regardless of status, felt that the rehabilitation hospital filled a psychiatric need. There was almost uniform agreement despite the possibility of job dissatisfaction in some cases. (2) The staff were keenly aware of their professional standing but were very modest about their role. We mean by this that they did not perceive their jobs in the rehabilitation hospital as being unique in the profession. This item was stated in a very cryptic way: "My job is just like any other." (3) The staff members at the same time were consciously aware that patients were more complex than commonly supposed, and that they were not always prepared to handle this psychological aspect of their work. They further thought that refresher courses might serve both ends, that is, (2) upgrade their professional status, and (b) help them better to understand the patients.

The key to the patient orientation was, in this respect, linked with a professional orientation, and those respondents who felt a need for greater understanding of patients marked "yes" to the items dealing with the need for education in their work (89 per cent agreement among the items).

Some statements were much less ambiguous in focusing upon a certain orientation over others. As an example, the item concerning the need for the rehabilitation hospital was stated clearly and reflected a production orientation in itself: "There should be a greater number of production facilities just like this one for the chronic patient." There was no disagreement; 20 per cent moderately agreed, 80 per cent strongly agreed. There was a tendency for the staff to disagree with the item pertaining to the necessity for some sort of uniform in the rehabilitation hospital. This question is interesting in that the uniformed psychiatric nurse is a point of debate among many American hospital nursing administrators and nurses themselves, and patients have been queried as to their preference for uniforms for nurses. In percentages, this item was found to have the following distribution ($N = 52$):

32%	18%	14%	20%	16%
Strongly Disagree	Moderately	Neutral	Moderately	Strongly Agree

These data were separated between the thirty-four uniformed and eighteen non-uniformed members of the staff. The following percentages indicate a tendency for greater agreement and less indifference among the uniformed personnel, but still this is a subject on which there was little uniformity of opinion. The clinic staff noticeably preferred the uniforms and felt the need for them.

The data support the assumption that the staff members themselves, through their experience in the program, shared with the

Uniformed (N = 34)

Strongly Disagree	Moderately	Neutral	Moderately	Strongly Agree
24%	14%	9%	29%	24%

Non-uniformed (N = 18)

Strongly Disagree	Moderately	Neutral	Moderately	Strongly Agree
50%	28%	22%	0%	0%

author his belief that such hospitals fulfill a basic requirement in restoring many patients to the community. This response was elicited regardless of the extent of contact the staff members had had with patients or their sophistication in psychiatric problems.

It was also found that particular emphases in treatment were centered in definite parts of the rehabilitation hospital structure. Tables E-1 and E-2 in Appendix E are evidence of this, but taking a specific item as an example might make this conclusion more graphic. We chose the rather dogmatic statement: "I feel that patient promotion to a more advanced unit should depend primarily on the amount of work he does." Generally, this item evoked either moderate disagreement or a noncommittal reply. The extremely small numbers allowed in a breakdown between the sections of the hospital can only serve as an outline, but the percentage distribution indicates more agreement in some areas than in others.

Intake Unit (N = 7)

Strongly Disagree	Moderately	Neutral	Moderately	Strongly Agree
0%	57%	14%	0%	29%

Chronic Unit (N = 4)

Strongly Disagree	Moderately	Neutral	Moderately	Strongly Agree
0%	75%	0%	0%	25%

Middle Unit (N = 5)

20%	20%	20%	40%	0%
Strongly Disagree	Moderately	Neutral	Moderately	Strongly Agree

Discharge Unit (N = 4)

50%	25%	25%	0%	0%
Strongly Disagree	Moderately	Neutral	Moderately	Strongly Agree

Nursing Administration (N = 5)

60%	20%	20%	0%	0%
Strongly Disagree	Moderately	Neutral	Moderately	Strongly Agree

Psychiatrists (N = 4)

0%	50%	25%	25%	0%
Strongly Disagree	Moderately	Neutral	Moderately	Strongly Agree

There is a higher proportion of disagreement among those at the top echelon of the nurses, who have somewhat less constant and direct working relationship with the patients, than among those we have theoretically, and because of their position, called "role models." A less firmly committed opinion existed among the medically trained staff. The three places where we find any measure of agreement that production, or how much a patient does, is the chief criterion for advancement is in the Intake Unit where assessment is made, in the Chronic Unit, and in the Middle Unit, where a higher production orientation was found. Of course, the data here are a part of the Middle Unit staff's orientation score, but it is important to note that the statement, as it was structured, did not meet with full agreement in the unit where this orientation was highest. It is interesting to compare these data with data on a less uncompromising statement.

Let us analyze the distribution regarding a less strongly-worded item and one which touches upon a basic philosophical concept underlying any rehabilitation hospital, whether it is designed for mental patients or unemployed people. This statement is: "Above all other considerations, work, no matter what one's ability or impairment, is a social responsibility." Some would call this the Protestant Ethic, and there seemed to be a fair degree of communality among the staff and the patients that work is essential. The overall distribution was:

6%	12%	10%	40%	32%
Strongly Disagree	Moderately	Neutral	Moderately	Strongly Agree

The separate distributions were:

Intake Unit

0%	14%	0%	57%	29%
Strongly Disagree	Moderately	Neutral	Moderately	Strongly Agree

Chronic Unit

20%	0%	0%	40%	40%
Strongly Disagree	Moderately	Neutral	Moderately	Strongly Agree

Middle Unit

20%	20%	0%	40%	20%
Strongly Disagree	Moderately	Neutral	Moderately	Strongly Agree

Discharge Unit

25%	0%	0%	25%	50%
Strongly Disagree	Moderately	Neutral	Moderately	Strongly Agree

Nursing Administration

0%	0%	20%	60%	20%
Strongly Disagree	Moderately	Neutral	Moderately	Strongly Agree

Psychiatrists

0%	50%	25%	25%	0%
Strongly Disagree	Moderately	Neutral	Moderately	Strongly Agree

We predicted a high proportion of agreement throughout the hospital staff, but we also find particularly strong agreement between the top nursing staff and the staff of the Intake Unit. The same essential distribution as on the previous statement occurs among the medically trained staff members. It appears that in those units where close supervision is necessary, the staff members depend upon explicit amounts of work as a guide in their determination of a patient's progress. In the unit where supervision is at a minimum, or at least an effort is made to reduce it, the staff members look at work as a responsibility, but not as a yardstick for their assessment of patients. Of course, advancement beyond this unit is not possible except to a job in the community, and the staff there would not perceive work within the unit in the same way as in the other units. The staff in the Discharge Unit also obtained the highest patient orientation score, which may generally reflect the attitude that work *per se* is of less importance.

There are no inconsistencies between attitudes held by the staff members in the various units and the particular type of patients or problems that characterize the units. The nature of the unit for intake patients would necessitate a close scrutiny of the work output, among other things, and we find that some staff members would consider this very important. It is in this unit where the dictum that work is compulsory, which the patient is told upon admission, is first translated into action. The pressure for promotion from this unit is greater because it is automatically the receiving unit for incoming patients. We do not imply that there is a cause and effect relationship, which could only be determined if these staff members were moved to other units and their attitudes changed.

It is interesting to compare the staff members' attitudes to those outside the rehabilitation hospital. In Chapter Seven, for example, we discuss the attitude that people in the community might have toward the rehabilitation hospital. One possible excuse for the existence of such a hospital would be its contribution to the economy of the region. In the course of the study, I was able to put this question to nineteen people who lived in the neighborhood of the hospital and who were not affiliated with it. The idea was stated in the following way: "Products assembled in a hospital by patients are highly important because they contribute to the national economy." The distribution was as follows:

Residents (N = 19)

0%	21%	15%	12%	52%
Strongly Disagree	Moderately	Neutral	Moderately	Strongly Agree

The agreement to this statement may reflect a current interest in the economy of the country, or it might show a high regard for the products, or both. It is interesting that such an idea is endorsed among the staff by half of those who work closely with the program, and a relatively small number were indifferent to the notion. Most interesting, however, is the differential endorsement between the staff and a sample from the community. The sample included housewives, a shopkeeper, a druggist, teachers, but no person who could be termed in competition with the hospital in its production.

SIX

The Educational Experiment

Lipsitt has expressed the opinion that a fundamental variable in hastening the release of the chronic mental patient from the psychiatric hospital is the extent to which the patient is consciously able to acknowledge his dependency upon the hospital (Lipsitt, 1961). In the summary of the series of investigations reported in Chapter 5 more long-stay than short-stay patients noted that they were independent. Lipsitt suggests that denial of dependency may be a problem in rehabilitation. If this is true and assuming that saying one is independent means just the opposite, our data indicate that the rehabilitation hospital may defeat its own purpose by enhancing the illusion of greater independence. An example of this unrecognized dependency is the idea (expressed by an occasional patient in the rehabilitation program) of constructing a manufacturing plant at the hospital site where patients would be the permanent work force. In this way the patients would be permanently attached to the hospital without the "threat" of open employment in the community. They could also maintain a feeling of independence from the stigma of being a mental patient living in a psychiatric hospital, as this type of institution is usually construed to be.

Dependency, therefore, is an important factor recognized by the staff of the rehabilitation hospital. They feel that the work done by the patient nurtures a feeling of dependency, which must be countered by a systematic program of presenting the world outside in meaningful and attractive terms. This program, which we call "the educational experience," is many ways part of routine work of the members of the staff, including the nurses who work with the patients on the hospital contracts. A more formal approach is given through a series of classes in health, hygiene care, and cooking. Teaching specific skills to the patient, such as typing or instruction in prerequisite course for academic degrees, is the traditional work of the educational therapists in most hospitals. In the hospital/factory, arrangements are made for the patient to learn these skills and to take required courses for degrees in the community schools or to help in conducting the business of the hospital.

There is a vast area of potential problems about which the patient may know very little and which he is ill-equipped to handle. These problems concern just those practices of modern living that are taken for granted by most people, but result in many confusing and anxious moments for the patient when he leaves the hospital.

These problems are similar to those that confront the elderly person or poverty victim who has not had to solve them for reasons other than hospitalization, such as age and lack of steady income. Keeping accounts, using self-operating elevators, knowing postage rates and telephone procedures are examples.

Sometimes these problems of uninformed people in a mechanized society are poignantly portrayed in one's personal experience. I recall coming to the assistance of an aged woman whom I found weeping outside a telephone booth. She wished to place a call but was afraid of the entire mechanism, even of stepping inside the booth. I was also certain that she'd have found the detailed information printed outside the booth incomprehensible. It is the task of the social re-education instructor to interpret, with understanding and compassion, the aspects of the world that provoke anxiety in such people.

This type of social problem confronts the staff person working at re-educating the chronic mental patient. The problem of re-educating a patient who has been in the hospital a long time poses more problems because (1) he has often been in the hospital for many years, and frequently he has had only brief visits home, which never afforded him the opportunity for involvement in these matters; (2) his family actively prevents him from managing his affairs in many cases because of the uncertainty of the outcome or because the parent hospital authorities have counseled them against it; (3) the mechanization and improvements of the tasks themselves have become more complex while the patient has been hospitalized, and certain procedures, such as obtaining unemployment compensation, have been altered; (4) the patient himself has become less interested in these matters because he has ceased considering them pertinent to his situation; (5) he is often too confused to retain the material given him for very long without reinforcement; (6) he may believe that learning these techniques brings closer his discharge, which in itself is threatening; (7) a long-term patient, particularly, may have no one to sustain the encouragement he needs after his discharge to make any effort along these lines worthwhile. Some patients may be intellectually incapable of performing the tasks once they have learned them. They are able to parrot the knowledge they have learned, but are not able to translate this knowledge into action.

It is in the area of rehabilitation of the subnormal that the work has been done thus far, and it was the assessment used in a program designed for these people that served as the impetus for this study.[1] We refer specifically to the work of Gunzburg and his associates at Monyhull Hospital. A visit by a member of St. Wulstan's social re-education staff to Monyhull proved beneficial. Gunzburg has devised an individual instrument that surveys an amazing variety of tasks in which a person must be somewhat proficient if he is to function outside the institution. The test uses many actual items to determine a profile of the patient's level of competence in these areas (Gunzburg, 1960). Competence is conceived on three levels and a checklist is made of the items failed and passed at each level. The nature of the test demands that periodic checks be made to update the answers to conform to changes in the area tested.

---

[1] To our knowledge, no attempt has been made to re-educate the chronic and psychotic mental patient in just this way. We modified our program slightly and matched the curriculum to the areas covered by the assessment used with the subnormal patients.

This record, called the Educational and Social Assessment Record, was given at the rehabilitation hospital before the substitute test was devised and administered for the purpose of the study. The several steps of the test took an hour and a half. (1) The patient was asked to write a letter and address an envelope to a relative or friend. (2) He was asked to fill out a prepared job application form. (3) He was requested to read aloud words commonly found on signs and notices in specified areas in the community; for women, this step had an alternative list. (4) He was instructed to identify actual coins and to make change according to standard problems. (5) He was given several problems in mental arithmetic. (6) He was given several questions of a temporal orientation nature, and a problem in planning a short journey and scheduling time in order to meet a prearranged appointment. (7) He was asked to figure a bus timetable. (8) The next questions related to the costs of postage for air mail, postcards, and such items. (9) These questions were followed by a series of questions involving functions of the post office (registered letters, packages), how to send money through the mail, use of the telephone (with a dummy instrument for demonstration purposes) with particular emphasis on the new dialing system. (10) He was then asked the reasoning behind income tax, and what sort of deductions were ordinarily possible. (11) He was asked the prices of and where one would purchase certain items that were very different from one another. (12) These questions led to an inquiry into what the patient understood about buying on a charge account and how to go about securing credit (some words of caution always accompanied these questions). (13) Ways of saving money were asked of the patient along with charges for this service. (14) The final questions were concerned with finding a doctor and first aid procedures in the event of an emergency.[2]

We have here an exhaustive standard interview and examination of the patient's knowledge unrelated for the most part to the

[2] Many of these questions and correct answers were unique to the British system, such as the functions of the post office. The rationale suggests that the content is adaptable to any society or country. One such program was being considered for a hospital in Ghana after the visit of one member of their staff to the program discussed here.

extent of his illness. This procedure had the advantage of pinpointing areas requiring educational attention, review, and remedial training. For experimental purposes, a test with a single index was required, for we wished to investigate which of two methods was more effective in teaching these chronic patients the content of the assessment. We wished to retain the division into areas of the original scale as much as possible to determine which areas were more extensively retained after the methods were used.

In Gunzburg's work, a rigid classroom structure with many intriguing mechanical aids is usually used. We felt that the class technique as described by Earl (1961) would be adequate for the subnormal adolescent or young adult, but would pose problems for our patients (and for adult poverty victims) for numerous reasons. For one, it would offer the person little opportunity to experience social interaction to counter the withdrawal and the tendency to be uncomfortable in such situations. For another, it would be insulting to his age in many cases. It would also be inconsistent with the rehabilitation hospital philosophy that otherwise emphasized adult responsibilities and performance. For these reasons, the classroom technique might not be effective for imparting the material to be learned. The alternative method was one that had been used successfully in adult training courses, that is, the group discussion method.[3]

Our task was to present rather informal material, such as the cost of a week's provisions and how to buy them most inexpensively, to patients who were uninterested in formal education, and, in some cases, had dropped out of school at an early age with unhappy memories.

The methods chosen for the experiment placed the two instructors in very different roles, according to the method used. The instructors were much more active and directive in the classroom, or

[3] We considered another method—programmed teaching with the machine—which we discarded because we felt that the complete absence of an instructor during much of the training period would be inconsistent with ideology of the hospital and would be of even less social benefit to the patient. It was also very doubtful that the patients could tolerate the time of inactivity necessary for the many frames that would be required for the entire program.

demonstration, method, and more passive and less directive in the discussion method. At times, the direction of one instructor over another was apparent in the former method, but care was exercised to share this leadership while the trials were in progress.

All groups were conducted by the same two instructors. The sessions were held in the same large room, which also served as a gymnasium. Replication of the experimental conditions enabled us to give the different types of instruction at the same time of the day, so that fatigue factors were counterbalanced. This is especially important in a hospital with an active work program. Both men and women patients participated, and they were from all areas of the rehabilitation hospital, although 38 per cent of the patients came from the unit where the most chronic and retarded patients worked. It was in this unit where most deficiency in these areas of social competence was thought to be shown, but testing indicated that patients in the pre-discharge unit achieved equally low scores.

In the demonstration method, the patients sat in a row before a table, behind which was a blackboard. These materials were situated at one end of the room. The instructors presented the information from prepared statements and in a prescribed order. At appropriate points in the presentations, the instructors used demonstration devices such as the dummy phone to show correct use of the telephone, or the telephone directory to show how to find a given number. The last session was devoted to questions and a summary of the material. Care was taken to include answers to all questions asked on the pre-trial assessment.

In the discussion method, attendance was also taken, but the patients sat in a circle and the topics were introduced from the framework of actual problems in daily living. The patients could take notes if they wished to do so, but few did. The discussions often ranged widely, but the instructors were careful to cover all of the material.

A third experimental condition alternated these methods from session to session. We wished to know whether mixing the two methods resulted in interference or a cumulative effect.

Two groups of patients served as the control group (no instruction), which tested whether the rehabilitation hospital environment itself, without training, would teach the patients the material in which we were interested. All patients had the same opportunity for community contacts; no group members differed in this respect.

A partial replication of this experiment was done in order to counterbalance fatigue factors by giving the different types of instruction at various hours during the morning. A total of sixty-six patient-students were taught in two twenty-session demonstration classes, two twenty-session discussion classes, two twenty-session alternate classes, and one class of each of these methods for half of that time, or ten sessions twice weekly. There was a control group for each of these twenty or ten session periods with assessments made but with no intervening instruction.

The replication of the twenty-session classes proved to be a wise maneuver because we would have been led completely astray by our initial results had we not repeated the procedure. We found that the discussion method was superior, followed by the alternate and demonstration methods in that order, as predicted. Contrary to this finding, repeating the course of instruction with a matched group of subjects brought about an entirely different result. The overall conclusion was that no single method was superior but that significant learning took place under all methods. Some patients revealed learning and retention after six weeks; others did not. Before reviewing the results of the experiment, we must mention some conclusions from the assessment instrument itself as a reflection of knowledge assumed to be important for self-maintenance. The longer the patient had been hospitalized, the less we knew as measured by the assessment; but the type of ward (restrictive or not restrictive), extent of community contact, and diagnosis bore no relationship to his test results. The more natively intelligent the person, the better his score.

The experiment proceeded with a variety of persons, men and women, young and old, from different units and work situations; all of their performances (choices on a multiple-choice test) improved by varying degrees. Some were able to recall the material after a month and a half; others forgot much of it.

For the longer period of instruction, discussion gave the

subjects a better means by which to retain the information they had learned and tended to bring all subjects to the same level of performance. We further found that people who had no classes but who were in the hospital/factory steadily increased their scores over a similar group in another larger institution a few miles away. We concluded that being in this type of hospital milieu contributed to this result. Both of these groups never improved their scores to the level attained by the subjects in the classes immediately after the period of instruction. We concluded that there were individual differences among the patients that interfered significantly with the educational process, or enhanced it, as the case might be. These differences were higher intelligence (resulting in greater learning) and less overt and socially disturbing illness. Inability to retain what was learned after a longer interval was associated with longer accumulative institutionalization.

A selection of more intelligent persons who are not obviously withdrawn or "socially embarrassing" (see Appendix G), and who have had relatively few years away from the larger society, produces better results no matter which method of education (among those chosen here) is used. The less intelligent and frankly defective persons learn, providing that they are not also acutely ill. Their learning is above their individual base line, but they do not reach the level of the more intelligent. They can likewise retain if they have not been institutionalized for a long time.

We believed that an analysis of each item on the Assessment Test would reveal which type of information was learned most easily, regardless of the method of instruction. We compared the items that had a low correct scoring for all subjects before instruction and showed an increase after instruction with those that had many correct responses before instruction and no increase after instruction. We selected for the first category, arbitrarily, those items that had fewer than eight patients selecting the correct responses; we selected for the second category those items that had twenty or more patients selecting the correct response. Six items showed a consistent increase of correct responses between testings according to this criterion. There were twelve items that almost everyone knew and did not learn further through instruction. The items that were unknown and learned were those that were out of the patients' immediate experience (such as the first aid hints), or things that changed in themselves during the instruction period (such as a raise in television license rates). The commonly seen or used item (such as what P.M. denoted, or the color of mail boxes) were initially known and statistically no increase was possible. There were certain items that caused more difficulty than others when retention scores were considered. When the test was given at the time of the follow-up, the number of correct scores for these items was lower than when it was first given, and after an increase in number of correct choices immediately after instruction. These items were characterized by their detail, such as what is the second—as opposed to the first—thing one must do to make a telephone call, or who gives one the "first sick note" when ill outside the hospital. The problem appeared to be, in a very real sense, one of recalling exact procedures in a series of events compounded by the difficulty in relating oneself to the world outside the hospital. Many patients, for example, reverted to the hospital rather than a local physician as the authority where one would procure a "sick note." Those items that showed the greatest amount of retention were again those commonly seen and shared in the daily life of the patient both inside and outside the rehabilitation hospital.

These conclusions are not as simple as would at first appear, and more subtle influences not tested by our assessment test warrant further discussion.

Aside from the material the patients learned through the classes, changes in behavior were noted in the group sessions. One group, for example, was composed only of men from the chronic unit, where the most deteriorated patients lived and worked. One of these six men, an older patient, took it upon himself to shepherd another, younger man to the group each morning. This relationship began to become routine after two weeks and continued for several more sessions, until the younger patient was able to remember to leave his work and to come to class unassisted. These two men were not particular companions outside the program.

It was necessary to give at least one person in each group

a note of reminder, telling him where and at what time the group met. These patients usually continued coming to the classroom beyond the termination of the sessions for their group. They had to be asked to return to the workshop. After two or three times the patients would no longer appear.

Prompting between patients during the group meetings was a common practice, and this was especially noticeable in a group of women who attended with a very withdrawn man. Each of these women prompted him without any show of annoyance at his retarded responses.

We found it useful and almost mandatory to review, at the beginning of each session, the points that had been made during the previous session. For classes in which we used the demonstration method, we put these points on the blackboard for all to see.

Rapport was established in all of the groups by the simple exchange of personal data and points of view. Some of the patients were interested in telling the instructors about their communities, but few referred to the hospitals from which they came. It was only in the context of comparing facilities and adequacy of the meals served to them that this subject was ever discussed. It was not that the patients were embarrassed about their hospitals or were attempting to forget this phase in their lives, but rather that there seemed to be a tacit assumption that all hospitals were the same, save this one.

Visitors to the group sessions were permitted, and on these occasions the sessions became somewhat more interesting and the patients became more animated—whether because the patients wanted to display their knowledge to the visitor, or because the visitors became involved in the group, or because the instructors desired to "put their best foot forward" before the visitor is not known. The visitors came from both inside and outside the hospital.

These visitors usually asked the instructors one question, which can be paraphrased as follows: "We have seen you spending time and effort with these patients. Many of them seem to have learned a great deal. But how can you be sure that they will be able to use the knowledge and the confidence you have given them?"

Restated, this question concerned the concept of volition: "Assuming that volition is lacking among the chronically ill, does your program help them in overcoming this handicap?"

Experience with long-hospitalized patients working in an industrial rehabilitation hospital leads one to assume that these patients can function in the community more easily than they actually can. A patient can receive and count his pay for work performed, and may even be able to deposit this money within the hospital at the appropriate place and complete the necessary forms for withdrawals. He is confronted with an unfamiliar act within familiar surroundings. Purchasing a savings certificate in a post office where he is known is a step beyond, but still in familiar territory. Opening an account in a bank in which he has never been is utterly foreign to his experience. It is difficult for the mental patient particularly to cope with such a novel situation. The instructors of a training program must recognize a tendency to overgeneralize what is learned in the hospital to slightly different procedures. Preparing the patient for every eventuality, therefore, becomes a monumental task, and, without a patient who is intellectually capable of showing the required flexibility in thinking, it is nearly hopeless. A hopeless situation for the instructor is doubly hopeless for the patient who is motivated toward the instruction in the classes, but is incapable of implementing what he is learning.

It is not always the most intelligent patient who profits from the training we have described, as our data show. Likewise, it is not only the least "institutionalized" patient who profits (see Appendix G). Another ingredient was more important among those whose scores showed learning. This factor could roughly be termed "motivation to learn." One male patient, for example, showed keen interest in the cost of foreign mail when he realized that he could write to a brother who was living in Canada. His involvement in this small part of the course of instruction led him to inquire about ways of doing things in other countries and from this angle he began to grasp this knowledge as it applied to his own country. He was rarely observed, however, to leave the hospital and go into the community.

A possible measure of level of motivation in class (although absence of social withdrawal and level of intelligence were associated with this behavior) was the number of times a given patient indulged in the involuntary prompting discussed earlier. Our patient scored high on this index, but, in following this patient's progress after his instruction was concluded, a further, more relevant problem to community adjustment was unearthed. This problem— which we will term "volition"—occurred in the cases of all patients to varying degrees.

The docility that lack of volition connotes was found in the patients' readiness to agree to the instructors' suggestions and their procrastination in carrying them out. Advice was not given explicitly in many cases, but possible avenues of action were explored when a patient brought up a problem relevant to the topics discussed in the class.

Nevertheless, the reaction of the patients to other events in the hospital did not always mirror the docility that characterized many of the patients in the group situation. They were eager to arrange trips from the hospital and to change from one job to another in the course of their work.

In some cases, an undercurrent of anger and disgust erupted in their conversation in the discussion method condition. These expressions of displeasure were usually couched in criticisms of staff members who were interpreted as exercising control over the patients' work, but who were relatively distant from the actual operation of that work—for example, the plant manager.

Some patients complained that they saw in the discussions little relevance to obtaining employment. Two techniques were used to circumvent the academic unreality of the instruction and to place it within the experience of the patient. One technique was employing the use of demonstration telephones, charts, and forms to fill out. The second technique was to role-play actual situations the patients might meet while living in the community.

In some cases, the patients' tendency to diminish the volition and ingenuity required of them was patently clear. One such example was their response to the following problem: "You (the patient) are returning to the rehabilitation hospital from a weekend visit and find that you have spent more money than you had intended.

You are in a small village some miles from the hospital and the village has a telephone box. What would you do?" The answer that was sought involved telephoning the staff at the hospital for aid and reversing the charge for the call. Rather than make this effort, most of the patients in the group solved the problem by seeking the aid of the police. This solution was reasonable, but it placed the responsibility for the problem into the hands of another authority. Another example of the patients' relying upon others to substitute for their lack of volition was asking the rehabilitation hospital chaplain to buy them new shoes and to write letters to their relatives despite their ability to do these things for themselves. This indicated a healthy and growing relationship with the chaplain, but was counter to the staff's encouragement that the patients do these things for themselves. Our observation of patients buying different items in the community showed that they were capable of doing these things.

Recognition that lack of volition was a principal problem led us to develop a system of journeys into the community on which the instructor assigned to the social education program would accompany the patients. Accompanying chronic mental patients into the community is not new. It has been usually viewed as an outing and a respite from the ward routine for both patients and staff.

The journeys attached to the program in the rehabilitation hospital were, first of all, only for those patients for whom they were deemed necessary. The following progression was followed: (1) The patients were taken in groups of four or five for their first trip and shown the various public buildings and shops in the community. They paid their own fare on the transport and usually had a refreshment with the staff member before returning. (2) On the next trip the patients were asked to buy something for the workshop or for themselves and they went, not as a group, but alone in the company of the instructor. (3) On the final trip, after two or three of these journeys, the patients were sent alone on some errand. The patient was finally observed wherever possible to determine how often he went to town. This topic frequently was mentioned when the staff reviewed the patient's progress.

Volition is defined as the power, or act, of choosing or making a decision, and has been analyzed under the concept of "will." An example for the purpose of this analysis is the patient's decision to make a journey into the community in order to purchase something unobtainable in the hospital. Several assumptions are made in this single instance: (1) It is assumed that the patient possesses the motor essentials to perform the act. This was determined by taking the patients in a group and observing them in the process of making the journey. (2) It is assumed that there is a purpose for the act. This was handled by linking the journey in a meaningful way to the function of the hospital. (3) It is assumed that there is a freedom of decision, and, without becoming overly involved in the philosophical implications of the problem, the attraction of the act was emphasized in discussion, circumscribing what could be obtained within the hospital, and continuation of "field trips" in the company of other patients and members of the staff. Attraction was also enhanced by giving the patients the necessary information, such as costs and places to go, that would reduce their uncertainty of performing the act successfully. It might be said with justification that the problem facing the staff of the rehabilitation hospital was to find ways not of coping with irrational acts, but of stimulating action.

In pursuing our method of dealing with the problem, we realized that there existed few recent research reports that treated the concept of volition as such.[4] There were, however, several conclusions in the literature that were relevant once the problem was stated in terms of decision-making, choice behavior, or stimulus input.

One of the more salient studies was Haas' finding that mere "openness" of the hospital environment failed to correct an essential passive orientation of the patients (Haas, 1963). This is confirmed in the experience of those who worked in the rehabilitation hospital. Active encouragement was mandatory for some patients to leave the grounds.

[4] One possible exception in Arieti's analysis of the catatonic schizophrenic being plagued by imagined and ego-threatening results once a position of responsibility is taken (Arieti, 1961). Few of the patients in the rehabilitation hospital were mutely catatonic. The taking of responsibility, however, aptly describes the program, and ego function may be disrupted in cases where agitation followed a trip. There was little evidence that this occurred.

Did the nature of the rehabilitation hospital help the patients to become intellectually able to learn from the trips?

Hamilton found that IQ ratings based upon the Mill Hill Vocabulary and Progressive Matrices increased for the patients who worked in workshop settings compared with those who were treated in occupational therapy units (Hamilton, 1963). This result was viewed as encouraging, inasmuch as workshop settings dominated the hospital and intellectual factors were thought to be involved in the problem of volition. The rehabilitation hospital was geared toward maximum increase of whatever intellectual functioning existed. Bearing in mind that there was no control group with which to compare results, we tested sixteen patients with the Wechsler Adult Intelligence Scale after they had been in the hospital an average of two years. There was an eighteen-point increase in their full-scale IQ scores, a thirteen-point increase in their verbal-scale scores, and a twenty-one-point increase in their performance scale scores. A greater increase among the performance items as compared with the verbal items might be attributed to the emphasis placed on manual dexterity and speed in the work of the factory.

The majority of the patients in the supervised trips were schizophrenic. Previous studies have shown that withdrawn schizophrenics focus much less on novel than on familiar objects (McReynolds, 1963), but that chronic schizophrenics (as opposed to acutely ill schizophrenics) were better at recognizing ambiguous stimuli at an earlier stage, and more importantly, recognized cognitive similarities (Draguns, 1963). It would seem from the latter study that the patients would recognize a familiar, distant red light as denoting "stop" at the traffic crossing more quickly than the instructor because the normal subjects in the experiment performed less well than the patients! When one considers the verbal interaction that accompanies the type of journeys that were designed, studies of verbal reinforcement become relevant. Chronic schizophrenics appear to respond to overlearning much more extensively than previously thought (Johnson et al., 1964). Schizophrenics also respond to stress with improvement in problem solving (Cowden, 1962), so that facing the journey alone was thought not to be detrimental to the learning process.

There are fewer studies related to the techniques of assisting the patients in taking the desired initiative. The fact that the problem exists was documented by Sidle, Acker, and McReynolds (1963), who found experimentally that schizophrenics as a group showed less active "stimulus-seeking" behavior than non-schizophrenics. Schooler's study was pertinent in demonstrating that schizophrenic patients, and particularly men, were extremely hesitant in opening themselves to social interaction (Schooler, 1963). Our observations showed that the male patients in the rehabilitation hospital were less likely to find friends and acquaintances on their own than female patients.

At least one study deals directly with the correction aspect of the problem. The study was cast in terms of incentives for motor and verbal tasks. MacDonald and Sheehan (1962) found that, on motor tasks such as walking to the bus stop (on the journeys), schizophrenics responded least to group encouragement and most to a concrete reward. On a verbal task, such as asking the bus conductor for directions, individual encouragement was most effective. As it was planned, the program of journeys combined these two methods: the patient was presented with a specific item to purchase (a concrete reward for a motor task), and the instructor accompanied him through the interaction process of dealing with the problem (individual encouragement for a verbal task).

Loss of volition due to long-term hospital inactivity is more profound than abulia, or absence of initiative, which is ascribed to intrapsychic conflicts. The patient not only is incapable of following through with a planned course of action, but is aware that action of any kind is permissible. Permission is either not granted or granted by forces outside himself, like the hospital authorities, *in addition to* forces within. It is the purpose of a resocialization program to extend the sphere of activity and to tell the patient what is possible to do. An action program in the company of the instructor, after the formal education, gives the patient confidence in carrying out self-motivated actions.

We would like for a moment to concentrate on a series of studies that have been carried out by Bruner and his associates at Harvard on the cognitive development of children aged five to nine.

The results of one such study by Sonstroem (Bruner, 1966) is of particular relevance to our discussion here. Sonstroem found that her subjects were able to acquire an appreciation of the notion of conservation of solids (modeling clay) only when both subject manipulation and experimenter labeling, or verbal explanation, were introduced into the condition. In Bruner's terms, enactive representation was thereby encouraged by the former and symbolic representation was encouraged by the latter technique. We believe that a similar situation occurs in a re-education program such as we have described in this section. There are certain assumptions that need verification, such as the implicit association between the cognitive functioning of the non-conserving child and of the adult chronic psychotic. Nevertheless, there is a striking procedural similarity between the techniques we employed. Consider, for example, the possibility that manipulation (of the environment), such as trips into town with an instructor whose role might be that of a "labeling agent," is similar to the condition Sonstroem found so powerful in her experiment. It is possible that not only cognitive growth but motivation toward action can be promoted by such a combination of representations.

In determining the effectiveness of the program, the author divided the patients who participated in the program into two groups: (1) those who had been given the classwork only, and (2) those who had been given the classwork and had been taken on the field trips with the instructor. The nurses furnished information about the number of times these patients were observed to go to the community on weekends. The same information was obtained about those patients who had served as the control group in the experiment reported in Appendix G and from where our conclusions are drawn. A period of four consecutive weekends was used as a basis for these data, and notation was made as to whether the patients went to town with another patient or alone. "Going to town" is not the only criterion of effectiveness for a program with such a scope as this one, but this was one of the points that was emphasized in the classes and in the review of the patients' progress as being desirable, and one action that the patients were all equally free to do. Only those patients who, as far as it was known, had never made the trip were included in the tabulations.

Two points were assigned for every solo journey, and one point for a journey in the company of other patients. We were aware that some patients went to town with friends who were quite capable of making the journey alone. If this seemed to be the case, these patients were not included.

Most of the patients were men. There were five patients in the class-plus-supervised-trip category, of whom three continued to make solitary trips to town and one went twice during the period in the company of another patient (who was in one of the classes but who had not been taken on one of the supervised trips). The mean score for this group was 5.2; the mean score for the six patients who had the classes but not the trips was 2.0, because one patient earned the score of eight (he began going to town alone for some unexplained reason), and two other patients went together twice during the period. Three of the six control-group patients in the foregoing study had never been to town. One of these patients went on three consecutive Saturdays, so that the overall score for these patients was 1.0.

The fact that the assessment scores of the members of the control group continued to increase was not reflected in their going to town more often. The introduction of the planned journeys served to increase town journeys in the other groups.

These results are encouraging and lead us to conclude that such a program established a pattern of going to town. In talking with two of the patients who had participated in the program, I noted that some of their comments were related to volition: "I decided to stop in . . . ; I stopped for . . ." On another occasion, a patient corrected me on the price of an item that we had happened to discuss in one of the sessions. Journeys into town accompanied the sessions for a few patients who had established the pattern by themselves.

It is important to point out that none of the foregoing studies basically altered the organizational structure of the hospital. The Social Re-education Program, nevertheless, was conducted on a different basis.

The true test of the worth of such a program as we have analyzed in alleviating one of the major problems of American society, that is, the presence of poverty victims, is in its application. Before the outcome of such an application can be predicted, the mechanics of rehabilitation must be thoroughly understood. The theoretical basis for such an approach and its implications for the restoration of the poor through such an approach are discussed in the following chapters.

 *SEVEN*

Social Role
Theory

For the overall model of social behavior and behavior change, the hospital/factory uses social psychological concepts related to clinical practice. These concepts are *self-image, role model, work role,* and *reference group.* A presentation of the theory, with a discussion of relevant research, will precede an analysis of the

way in which the theory clarifies the work of the hospital.

We have discussed some of this material from a research point of view in the general evaluation of the hospital/factory as a "going concern" in Chapter 5. At that time, we were primarily interested in the role of the nurse. The role of the nurse in the "total institution," despite the role's avowed ambiguity, is often described as that of a "Florence Nightingale." The traditional role model is well prescribed and conforms generally with the layman's view of the nurse.

⋅§ ROLE MODEL WORK AND SELF-IMAGE ?⋅

The role model of the nurse in the hospital/factory, however, is different from the traditional role model; the nurse must be a work expert to the patient as well as one who imparts a feeling of competence to him. In his role as work-companion, the nurse provides for the patient the role model of a productive, integrated person.

Explicit training to be such a role model is absent in professional curricula, and the administrative staff of the rehabilitation hospital relies on its

115

selection of productive, well-integrated, and ambitious applicants to fill this need. A similar emphasis on these qualities has been described by Colarelli and Siegel (1966) in their work with nursing assistants at the Topeka State Hospital.

We have stated that introducing work into the institution changes not only the role of the nurse but also the role of the patient, and a new relationship is formed between them. This relationship is a fluid one; the nurse's role shifts between mentor or role model in the world of work and advisor or confidante in the social environment surrounding the work role. We will next consider how the work role (Vroom, 1964) affects the self-image of the person, and, specifically, of the chronic mental patient.

We adopt the Gestalt psychologist's framework of figure and ground relationships, but in a historical, not an ahistorical perspective. The interaction of personality and environment constitutes the ground; and the image the person holds of himself constitutes the figure. It is the image upon which we focus, for without a change in the image any change in the person's behavior is not meaningful. "Image" means, for our purposes, something reflected. In our interpretation, it is the experiencing self reflected on the ground of an environment populated by others. The dimensions of personality are also ground against which the image of self is mirrored.

To understand how this operates, let us put ourselves in the place of the patient or the unemployed person. We believe that we are "sick" because we are uncomfortable when we find ourselves in an enclosed place. We have been told that we suffer from claustrophobia, and we are presently in a mental hospital. If we are poverty victims, we are "lazy" because we are not working in a society geared to productivity. We then act out these images.

The word "chronic" means characterized by long duration; we may safely predict that a chronic condition will not change. It frequently becomes a norm in itself. The chronically unemployed are a predictable segment of labor statistics. Chronic patients (or poverty victims) are persons in whom change is unexpected, and therefore unlikely. It is predicted that they will chronically remain in their present status within the framework of society. This image is relatively enduring and self-perpetuating, and is created by the mental hospital environment and the expectations of the society. The enduring quality comes about principally because of the unchanging nature of the ground.

It is true that many patients' conditions change when they remain in the hospital, but, at the same time, many others may leave and become what is known as "individual chronic wards" in the community. These patients show the same social aloofness and inertia that they displayed on the ward. This situation attests to the stable nature of the self-image when high expectations do not enter to improve the chances of good adjustment (Freeman and Simmons, 1963).

The work role in a rehabilitation setting is relatively enduring because of the nature of cooperation introduced between an "expert" and a "novice," and the consistent relationship between the role model and the person being directed toward the job to be accomplished. This does not imply a power relationship. The work role is also a uniquely recurring situation. The recurring nature of the situation with its rhythms of work, relaxation, and rest enables the person to develop a stable and enduring self-image.

Our approach is an optimistic one based upon self-expectancies and the change of ground and figure relationships. This does not mean that figure and ground alternate in the configurational sense, but that the environmental ground can be manipulated, and the change in figure, or self-image, will follow.

Rehabilitation is not defined entirely as a change in self-image. Rehabilitation, or returning to the community, includes much more. It implies, however, that the person thinks his rehabilitation is possible in his personal future, and that he will act to carry it out. This attitude may be formed by the rehabilitation process itself. We must also assume that the person is able to conceptualize a future and is mentally equipped to understand the necessary steps in achieving rehabilitation. Rehabilitation of this kind also necessitates a change in self-image, a change that is consistent with this new social role. Rehabilitation encompasses a concept of change, and an ability to relate the end of a process to the beginning. The person must, therefore, be able to compare what he believed himself to be before the rehabilitation process began to what he believes himself to be (his self-image) at the present moment.

Self-image changes with the experience of achieving. The opportunity to perceive achievement in oneself is a pivotal point in rehabilitation. For this reason, let us evaluate achievement as a psychological phenomenon.

Investigators have paid no small amount of attention to individual achievement as a psychological motive (McClelland et al., 1953). Because many of these investigations (and even here we refer only to the more relevant ones) have been in educational settings, much of this attention has been directed to academic achievement, and not to achievement among the mentally ill or chronically unemployed. One concept explaining the lack of academic achievement is the absence of another person with whom the poor achiever can associate academic success and with whom he can identify (Kagan, 1958). Kolb reports experiments with a program designed to raise the achievement motivation of highly intelligent but low achieving adolescents (Kolb, 1965). The characteristics of the desired person—that is, the person whose achievement is commensurate with his potential—were taught by a series of several techniques, only one of which was identification. We await a separation of these variables. In Kolb's study, a highly visible counselor was used, a time limitation was placed upon contacts with the counselor, and expectations in line with the purpose of the program were outlined to the subjects. An individual can also learn through emulation of a role model, whether he admires the role model or not, as long as he is rewarded by the role model. This has been shown by Bandura and his associates (1963), who have studied imitation within the framework of behavior theory. The investigators in these studies used children as subjects. Suffice it to say that the principle of training through emulation of other persons in these studies is similar to the principle of training through emulation of the role model in a work role relationship and has, as a part of its rationale, the modification of overt, disruptive behavior. We have shown how all of these features are incorporated into the hospital/factory. The similarity between the two programs—Kolb's Achievement Motivation Training Program and the hospital/factory program—extends to Kolb's remarks concerning social class as differentiating between some experimental subjects and others. These results are not entirely in line with those presented in the study reported in Chapter 5, where we found no difference between "achievers" and "non-achievers" along this continuum. The effect of the family environment (subculture) to which the subjects in Kolb's study returned and in which they encountered differential expectations is, however, analogous to the environment surrounding the discharged patient. The pressures for achievement must be sustained by employers, roommates, and the like, for optimal success of any program of this type; these pressures may be equally necessary for those who have been wasted through being considered unemployable.

By age, intelligence, and, most certainly, mental stability, the groups contrasted here are strikingly different, but in general the theory is the same and should extend over populations.

Let us examine more fully what is theoretically permissible in a theory of role model. Some aspects of the theory are similar to the concepts formulated by other investigators with quite different populations.

Role Models as Norm-senders

The concept of a role model interacting with others in a work role as an explanation of what transpires in the hospital/factory environment suggests a definition of role similar to that proposed by Rommerveit (1955) in his study of a rural Norwegian community. Applied to our problem, Rommerveit's analysis shows how chronic unemployment of some people can be sustained over long periods of time. After a careful analysis of many definitions of the concept, he adopts Mead's rather than Coutu's definition. As Rommerveit points out, Coutu defines role in such a way that the behaver, or role-taker, acts in a prescribed manner, but alone, in a particular social position. Rommerveit suggests that the "generalized other," as described by Mead (1934), is necessary in the formulation, and that the person behaves according to set patterns expected by others. He says that social pressures are enduring. We suggest that these pressures are even more enduring when they are consistent, as they are for the unemployable, who others expect will be unable to find a job.

When a person begins to work, one of the most consistent of social pressures is that found in the work role. Change in type of work is important, but the role itself remains constant.

Rommerveit suggests further that a relationship exists between norm-senders and norm-receivers. Norm-receivers are defined primarily as individuals. These individuals share pressures as members of groups. Norm-senders may be formal or informal groups in his formulation.

In the structure of the rehabilitation hospital work role, both groups and the individual as a role model are used to effect change through the pressures they exert. We might call the role model a "norm-sender" except for the fact that he sends more than a single norm of expected behavior. The person, or patient, receives the role through the mediation of the role model, and this role may carry with it different norms, or behavioral patterns, within the rehabilitation hospital. The rehabilitation hospital must, therefore, be as heterogeneous as possible in its areas of work in order to establish the various norms expected by norm-senders in the larger community. It is true that the norms of punctuality, responsibility, and reasonable sociability are common to all work roles. Cleanliness on the job is one example of a norm not common to all work roles in the environment.

A molar analysis is necessary even to a greater extent when we consider the rehabilitation hospital as an entity for behavior change whether the person is mentally ill or not. For example, the milieu of the hospital, with its total emphasis on the workday of the person if he is mentally ill, suggests several questions about the manifestation and alleviation of the patient's symptoms. From a clinical point of view, the total culture of the hospital serves to alter the self-image of the person. This assumption is in keeping with the considerable research in the area of the interaction between the "normal" personality and culture (Whiting and Child, 1953). One way in which this interaction comes about is suggested by the theorists who have emphasized the role of the "significant others" in the formulation of the "self" (Mead, 1934; Sullivan, 1953).

True Self and the Self-image

Our frame of reference was influenced by Sullivan in his assumption of a true self and self-image dichotomy. Let us risk oversimplification by stating that Sullivan interpreted psychosis as an adaptation to the strain imposed on the tension system when there is an ascendancy of the self-image over the true self. This ascendancy resulted from the person's oversensitivity to the feelings and reactions of others and from his loss of contact with the reality of the true self. The person could no longer evaluate the true self by the measure of what he erected as a socially formed self-image.

During the course of the study reported in Chapter Five, we found that a self-image related to oversensitivity, "easily hurt," altered with stay in the rehabilitation environment. It is highly probable that, at the level of the self-image, normal people (such as the poverty victim) would respond in much the same way within the same environment. Sullivan's theory was derived from his painstaking and empathic understanding of abnormal people and was not based upon conclusions from an academic study of the normal person. Nonetheless, Sullivan's work is applicable to the normal person. Denial, for example, is a necessary and very prevalent mechanism in human affairs. There is sufficient justification to suppose that not only children but normal adults make many decisions in their lives on the basis of their self-image and denial of the true self.

The interpretation of psychosis in terms of the patient's self-image explains much of the behavior of chronic patients. Scher (1960), for example, studied the self-image of the schizophrenic within the framework of the phenomenal self and found that lack of others' expectations promoted feelings of disrespect for the self. Fagan and Guthrie (1959) found that the schizophrenic has the ability to conceptualize what is normal in others. After several years' hospitalization and lack of expectations from normal people, patients are noted for their felicity in an environment unacceptable to the "outsiders." The volunteer worker who visits the hospital twice weekly is unable to understand the chronic patient's seeming obliviousness to the constraints placed upon him. When a number of patients on the ward begin to engage in a day program with work schedules in the community, the reaction among many other patients is uneasiness. This uneasiness is sometimes shared by the staff members, whose image of the patients is disrupted. Other patients express the hope to return to the responsible, well-paying jobs they may have held before their admission. The statements made by these patients are noted in the case records as "unrealistic aspirations" or "denial of illness." Scaling down these hopes for the future, or confronting the patients with the true self as judged by others, with the true skills and the true liabilities, is a delicate process; it sometimes results in the patient's becoming even more disillusioned when the staff does not exercise caution.

The program of protective work which the rehabilitation hospital affords, accompanied by the complete armamentarium of modern psychiatry—that is, drugs, individual counseling and group psychotherapy, and organic procedures—is a method of true self-confrontation. The program is far from "work for work's sake."

Work is the human activity, however, that carries with it the most social approval in Western society; it is also the most public activity. From knowing about a person's occupation, or whether he has one, we can draw many assumptions about him. With a knowledge of sociology and a person's occupation we can sometimes make accurate generalizations about a wide range of activities, many of which only remotely relate to work.

In this hospital, the work role is cast in the central position, wherein the patient has the opportunity to see himself in the public realm of work. The rehabilitation hospital presents the patient with the chance to gauge success and failure in concrete terms. Many patients and many poverty victims remain apparently uninterested and uninvolved with work, and their self-images remain unassailed by the facts. And, in Sullivan's terms, the tension system is not threatened by a return to the true self. The self-image remains undisturbed.

In the case of the hospitalized patient, disturbance of the self-image does not mean disturbance emotionally, or exacerbation of symptoms. It means that what the patient believes himself to be runs counter to and is unaffected by a reality that he believes to be inconsequential to himself. Most patients do not adopt the "don't care" attitude that this remark implies; however, a great many who continue in the same hospital environment after remission find an unrealistic self-image the most satisfying explanation for why they are still in the hospital.

⋐ *CHANGE OF SELF-IMAGE* ⋑

The self-image of the chronic mental patient can be changed over the relatively short time he spends in the rehabilitation hospital. Many factors contribute to this change.

Tranquilization by medication affects self-image. Symptoms unchecked by medication may interfere with work activity and, therefore, the true capacity of self is not made known to the patient. On the other hand, heavy medication may dull activity and distort the picture in the other direction. Heavy medication may prolong a loss of true self-awareness. Medication can potentially block the staff's gaining an assessment of the patient's ability. The staff is unable to pass on to him, therefore, by means of their expectations, any valid assessment of his capabilities.

The attitude of the staff and the work of the hospital affects self-image. We have assumed that the "significant other" in the rehabilitation hospital is the particular staff member who is important to the patient. This does not mean that the staff member becomes a father or mother figure, although he may in some relationships. The "significant other" is a working member of the staff of the hospital and is important to the patient as a producer of tangible goods. The fact that the work of the hospital is manufacturing real goods for sale in the real world is important. The patient's horizons may even be broadened if he realizes that the goods are for export, and in the hospital plan described in Chapter 3, this information is not withheld from the patient; it enhances his self-image as a producer. The patient perceives the staff member less as a nurse than as a co-worker or a foreman, and begins to react to him according to this perception. The staff member oversees the operation and offers suggestions. He or she may sit by the depressed and weeping patient while the work is being falteringly accomplished. But the immediate contact is maintained through the "activity therapy" of a working medium alternating with recreation and discussion about the work.

The distribution of activities may emphasize one aspect of the perception of self over others. Unlike some assignments occurring in hospitals of the traditional mold, recreation is sharply separated from work in two distinct areas of activity for both patients and staff in the rehabilitation hospital. The patient may be known to be gifted with good voice or to be knowledgeable about a certain sport, but his self-image as a worker is not confused with other abilities, although they may be highly important for his rehabilitation. If it is shown beyond a doubt that he can make a reasonable livelihood in the entertainment field, private coaching may be made available. It is rare that the age of the patient warrants taking this avenue, and these interests are encouraged simply as avocations.

Experiments with normal subjects have revealed a change in self-concept, or self-image, after approval and disapproval expressed by an "expert." In one experiment that lasted six weeks, this effect was achieved, and was dependent upon the number of "doses" of approval or disapproval given by the "expert" (Haas and Maehr, 1965). Among hospitalized adults and retarded children, evidence shows that performance on an intelligence test improves along with a lessening of social withdrawal after a brief period of social motivation (Cozens, 1964; Skeels and Dye, 1939). From these lines of investigation, one would anticipate change in the self-image of a patient in the presence of an approving "significant other," or role model, and in an environment designed to promote productivity and social stimulation. We did find the anticipated change. We also found other changes in the social self-image not directly related to the work role; among them is a closer identification with one's biological sex, particularly in the situation where the work role and the type of work identified with a particular sex are similar.

ᴥᔥ MEASUREMENT OF SELF-IMAGE ᖷᴥ

We will first discuss how change in self-image was measured in our studies and what factors determine the change. Taking the judgment of the nurse who works closest with the patient as a basis for comparison, we can find the discrepancy between the patient's self-image and the nurse's image of the patient. If the images are congruent, we can assume that a harmonious relationship exists between the role model's image of the patient and the patient's evaluation of himself. This harmonious relationship between images should be more apparent among the achievers and those patients who have been in the rehabilitation hospital for a longer time than among those who are not achieving, or who have been newly admitted and who have not experienced the benefit of the model. The effect of a change in self-image should not only be toward greater social acceptability among achievers, but should also be directly reflected in those images of the patient held by the "significant others," or their role models.

When the basis of comparison for the self-image is two or more role models, we cannot assume that they are equal in this role for the patient. We need a more direct approach to ascertain which of these persons has most influence on the patient, for which purpose a sociometric study is required. We cannot assume that the judgments made by two role models about one patient will be closer to one another for patients of low achievement than for those of high achievement. It is more reasonable to suggest that interstaff judgments will be similar for patients who are more stable and consistent in their behavior, regardless of achievement in the hospital program.

The efficacy of the relationship between role model and patient in changing the patient's image of himself depends on the adequacy of the role model. A male patient cannot easily emulate a very insecure female nurse even when performing the same daily task in the work role. Attitude toward mental illness is also thought to be a major determinant in the effectiveness of the nurse as a role model, and we found this to be the case in some of the units of the hospital/factory.

The concept of the work role is central to the formation of a changed self-image. It is in this area that the emphasis is placed even before the patient is actually admitted, as described in Chapter 3. Patients anticipate a work role for themselves before admission to the hospital/factory. At the preselection interview with the patient, careful inquiry is made into the work history. The expectation for work is, therefore, formed early in the patient's rehabilitation.

The rehabilitation hospital uses concepts developed by psychologists in effecting a change in self-image. Schizophrenics are people who suffer from a self-image of non-productivity as well as from distortions in perception and ideation. Some evidence shows that self-image is not so static as one would assume in such a population, as shown by investigators working with schizophrenics. Periodic reinforcements, for example, consisting of staff appraisal, or "doses" (Haas and Maehr, 1965), are administered routinely to the rehabilitation hospital patient in the frequent reviews of his productivity and behavior. The patient is also made aware of perceived failure and achievement (Olson, 1958; Diggory and Loeb, 1962).

The data on which we are basing much of this argument were obtained from studies with schizophrenics. We are applying conclusions reached by the investigators in these studies to the population in the rehabilitation hospital because by far the largest group were schizophrenic and secondarily diagnosed as "chronic" and "quiescent." It is restated here that only situationally the chronic schizophrenic and the chronically impoverished are at all similar. They are assumed to be comparable only in their distress at being jobless.

The work role, like all conceptions of role, refers to the behavior of the person. Adapting to a work role does not depend as directly upon personality dimensions, such as being dominant rather than submissive, as it does on certain behavior tendencies, such as punctuality.

The disordered personality expressed in symptom behavior, or in psychological dimensions tested by self-reports, should resist change to a far greater degree than the self-image, because the dimensions are formed much earlier and are less amenable to environmental influence. In theory, the disturbance of the personality expressed in symptomatic behavior is manifested unchanged and concurrently with a change in self-image. There may be temporary distortion of the self-image due to confusion. Experimental evidence suggests, for example, that maladaptive responses are not easily altered among severe schizophrenics (Crumpton, 1963), whereas intellectual functioning is increased with an alleviation of symptoms, or maladaptive responses (Haywood and Moelis, 1963). This evidence suggests that the chronic mental patient in an environment where his actions are consistently evaluated by role models will not alter in basic personality. Change will occur in his expected work performance and in his self-image. However, we found that personality factors also change and these factors are likewise not as static as assumed.

Shift from a relatively low self-image to a higher one is not necessarily an indication of improvement as judged by the hospital staff. Again using schizophrenics as our reference group, at least one study has shown that patients defensively distort and raise their self-image and lower their concept of what they admire as an ideal (Hillson and Worchel, 1957). A defensive tactic such as this, which is a result of anxiety, is not rehabilitation improvement as we define it. A lowering or raising of an unrealistic self-image on a reality-oriented basis is improvement. For example, a shift toward a self-image that is lower but more congruent with the role model's image of the patient indicates improvement. This formulation is biased toward social perception, and shows our inclination to call mental illness basically a social illness in symptoms if not in etiology. We believe that social perception is also crucial in the behavior manifested by the chronically poor.

We assume that evaluation by the role model in the rehabilitation hospital will be similar to future evaluations by a foreman or a member of the community where the patient is to live and work. In order to check this assumption at the rehabilitation hospital, the nurses' evaluation of the patient is compared with the evaluations by an outside employer after the patient is placed.

The Mechanism of Change

Attainment of new norms of behaving in the work role depends upon the intentional instruction by and incidental learning from the role models whom the patients encounter in the rehabilitation program (Sarbin, 1954). The means by which change occurs

in norms within roles other than the work role may differ qualita-
tively from the means by which change occurs within the work role.
Intentional instruction can be specifically geared to the requirements
of the community to which the patient is to be rehabilitated, or to
the sex of the patient. It can be given through simple beauty hints
for female patients, or through placing the male patient in "male" environments, such as working on the hospital van in the company of
men. The subtlety of incidental learning is perhaps more important
in its lasting effect, and no explicit program of incidental learning
can be prepared. A beginning of a program is made in the rehabilitation hospital through the consistency of the behavior expected of
the patient in the work role.

      Change in self-image implies a spread of effect, particularly
in incidental learning. In this context, secondary roles are acquired
from the common work role that is the chief norm of the environment. We may present an analogy of casting a pebble into a pool
of water—the stagnant pool of the life experienced in the custodial
institution—and the concentric ripples that emanate from this source
and widen to include other surfaces. The vortex of this process is the
expectations of work. Following our analogy further, we can infer
that the last perceptible wave is the crystallization of the sex role
and the image of the self as masculine or feminine with the accompanying sexual attractions. Few patients may experience this as a
realization of their potentialities. But an assessment that includes as
many social roles as possible enables us to chart these roles in the
self-image and to infer the extent of self-image change that a
changed environment brings about.

      Self-image change is brought about in the hospital/factory
by the patient's being overtly judged by role models. In contrast,
being evaluated *covertly* is a part of the patient's life in the traditional mental hospital. *Overt* judgments about his progress are
rarely transmitted to him. Frequently, the only way in which the
patients in traditional mental hospitals can note a change in their
condition is through being told by the staff that additional medicine
will be given to them. The explicit manner in which the staff of the
hospital/factory offers the patients an evaluation, and not only the

content of approval or disapproval, helps to alter the self-image of the patient.

The Reference Group Concept

A theory of rehabilitation entails the use of the concept of the reference group (Sherif and Cantril, 1947). Such a reference group is assumed to operate as much in the life of the institutionalized person and in the life of the poor as it does in the life of the "normal" person. In the traditional mental hospital, a particular position in the staff hierarchy serves as the reference group for the members of the staff; it is to other members of his specialization that the individual member relates in his working day. Patients recognize particular individuals as belonging to this or that segment of the staff. An occasional patient, because of his education and past experience, is found to relate to the hospital staff as his reference group although he is not formally recognized as belonging to this group. Ordinarily, patients relate increasingly to the hospital population as mental patients with the passing of time in the hospital. The poor person sometimes thinks of himself as belonging to the "army of the poor," if he, as the poverty victim, is singled out as such. More likely he thinks of himself as alone in his misery. No one could be as poor as he is and his problems are unique.

In the hospital/factory, however, both the staff and the patients lessen these former affiliations to their respective reference groups. This occurs in the common act of work, or in the interaction accompanying a joint work role. A shift of reference group for both the staff member and the patient constitutes the merging of their former affiliations and the shift of the reference group (patient and staff member) to that of the "productive worker." The value and norms of the "worker" replace those of the staff member and the patient. This process is only possible to a degree, and the nurse, for example, still retains the self-image of belonging to one of the service professions.

The process of change is a gradual one for the patient. At many points in his stay in the rehabilitation hospital, he reverts to the behavior of a mental patient and the reference group of the psychiatric population. In the ideal rehabilitation hospital, this change in reference group is accomplished without confusion and subsequent loss of all self-identity for the patient. The change is to be found paralleling the change in self-image. The ideal rehabilitation hospital affords the opportunity of the enactment of both roles: the role of the worker in the factory and the role of the patient (the "sick role") in the clinic. These situations must be physically adjacent and perceptually articulate and, at the same time, psychologically distinct. This differentiation helps the patient to make the distinction himself, and, in time, to adopt and to incorporate the behavior of the worker.

The utility of the reference group as an explanatory concept is not new (Newcomb, 1950). In Newcomb's elaboration of the concept, however, positive and negative reference groups are distinguished. A negative reference group is defined as one that is actually opposed by the person. The loss of the former reference group by the rehabilitated mental patient, or poverty victim, does not suggest that he is opposed to this reference group, but merely that this reference group has become latent. The impoverished person and patient may find relating to his particular reference group a help in time of stress or an excuse for failure. The new reference group and the role of worker may always be in jeopardy, and the strain of relating to the work role may be greater than the anxiety of thinking of himself as a patient. This state of affairs may be more apparent in the person when the role of worker is clear and direct, as in an impending job interview.

Life in the institution ordinarily offers the patient scant opportunity to formulate vocational expectations in a realistic manner. As a compensatory maneuver to combat the self-image of mental patient, the patient may think himself more valuable to others vocationally than he really is. Unrealistic expectations as well as a "sick" self-image are characteristic of the psychiatric patient. As the patient develops the role of worker, or of producer in the bona fide world of work, he becomes able to test his motor skills and aptitudes against those of others, especially those of the role model, and expectations for his vocational future become more realistic. Patients, for example, show an acute awareness of which jobs pay more and which jobs they perform best in a series of contracts in the rehabilitation program. If the discrepancy between the patient's performance as he appraises it, or as it is evaluated for him by the role model, and his expectations is too great (according to cognitive dissonance principles), a denial of the authority of the role model may result, and his unrealistic expectations are over-evaluated still more (Festinger, 1957), resulting in a failure of the rehabilitative program for this patient.

The environmental approach as a framework in which to analyze rehabilitation consequently requires analysis of how the environment affects (1) the patient's reference group, (2) his self-image, (3) the realistic-unrealistic nature of his vocational expectations, and (4) the congruence of his self-image with the image that the significant role model has of him. The patient's self-image can be compared with his actual placement in the rehabilitation program. Unrealistic self-appraisals can be discovered when, for example, the patient sees himself as "very productive," and sees his vocational reference group as civil engineers, while he is actually rated highly unproductive by his role model in the workshop, and he is being considered for transfer as a person unlikely ever to earn his living outside an institution.

The tensions incurred by introducing pressure for achievement may temporarily lower the person's image of himself. The "institutionalized person" who is a candidate for a rehabilitation hospital is often completely inured to the demands of a society that has achievement as one of its norms. These demands pertain not only to occupational achievement, but also to relative success in marriage, rearing a family, and getting along with one's neighbors. The means of achieving are ordinarily acquired through a lifelong process of social interaction, and many patients are hospitalized because of their psychotic reaction to the pressure of these demands. We would tentatively assume that the patient who has once experienced achievement before he became ill will have a fairly high level of achievement in the rehabilitation hospital. Attainment will be harder for one who has never achieved. A process of "disachievement" commences when the patient is hospitalized and forgets the tensions surrounding achievement. Environmental rehabilitation arouses these tensions again. Each day brings a step-by-step increase in the accomplishment of the contract. The investigators of this area (McClelland *et al.*, 1953) have never applied their theoretical expectations to the rehabilitation process. We are taking the liberty of doing so.

The lack of overt competition between individual patients and between groups of patients in the hospital/factory keeps tension down to a tolerable level. Groups of patients working on the same task may be given deadlines to meet, but these are shared experiences. The equilibrium of the role model is important in allaying the anxiety of the entire group. Another factor is the regularity of the reward for effort. Although the use of different frequencies in the reward of money has failed to produce any change in productivity (Phillips, 1965), group rather than individual working situations have been found to enhance overall productivity and satisfaction with the group (Query, Moore, and Lerner, 1966). The presence of other patients working together not only allows the patient to see that the task has meaning for others as well as for himself, but enables him to be regularly rewarded in the presence of others and with those who worked with him on the task.

Some chronic patients retain a premorbid compulsiveness that makes work of any kind prolonged agony. Others are unable to complete tasks, and the tension aroused from an incompleted task only heightens their anxiety (Zeigarnik, 1927). These are special problems designated as psychoneurotic, and individual task situations are required to assess these persons. Assessments in both individual and group tasks prove that working in a group lessens these conditions and the group norm prevails. The over-voluble person may impede by his talk the work of the group; an individual placement may be more beneficial both to the person and to the group, not to mention the completion of the task. All of these problems necessitate a thorough evaluation in task situations administered to the patient.

A feeling of achievement in the work role and a change in self-image are dependent upon such factors as morale. Morale on the job is influenced by home conditions, such as the advent of an unwelcome relative, and individual variables, such as one's general mental health. The motivation *to work* is much more complex and attempts to analyze it have been made from various frames of reference. We are not concerned directly with the theory of work, but how the material that has been assembled can be used to give meaning to the work of the rehabilitation hospital, which is to encourage *motivation toward working* among chronic mental patients and chronically unemployed people.

Herzberg, Mausner, and Synderman (1962) studied morale from the point of view of a factors-attitudes-effects complex as a unitary concept. Their approach was idiographic and they questioned individual workers from many plants of different sizes concerning high and low morale levels in their careers. Their results lend credence to our thesis that an environmental approach is fruitful. They managed through exhaustive questionnaires to isolate factors that, although not associated with the job, contributed to job dissatisfaction. They called these *backdrop* factors. The factors that were most related to job unhappiness were called matters of *hygiene,* for example, physical working conditions, benefits, security, interpersonal relationships, and supervision, to name a few. When complaints were expressed and morale was low these factors came to the fore. When morale was high, the workers focused upon a more personality-centered factor, self-realization, or discovering anew one's job potential and occupational identity derived from this subjective experience. At a low point in morale level, another interpersonal factor, inequity of salary, was a greater source of dissatisfaction than actual amount of salary.

These and other results from investigations of this sort are important to us in forming guidelines for the management of the rehabilitation hospital. It is necessary to maintain high morale among staff in the rehabilitation hospital as it affects not only their clinical function, but, as in any factory, their task function.

It is important to our concept of a role model that morale will be equally high among patients and staff; where it is not high, proper analysis can be made both at an individual and a work-group level. If the patient's job satisfaction is very low and the role model's is very high, very little understanding through the work role can be achieved. In this situation the role model should turn his attention to the patient and away from the task at hand. He should evaluate these "hygienic" factors described in the cited research and correct the factors that can be altered, and interpret others to the patient. When morale is raised so that the patient is able to experience the self-realization of work, the business of rehabilitation can be resumed. It is more in keeping with our theoretical position to say that the process of building morale when it is low and capitalizing on it when it is high is the means by which rehabilitation is brought out.

⋞§ THEORIES OF MOTIVATION §⋟

To the person who has been unable to support himself with gainful employment, work in and of itself brings about change in his self-image.

There are several theoretically sound reasons that have been suggested to explain why work as an effortful activity is a motivator and increases morale (Lewis, 1965). Paying a small amount of money for a great amount of work, as during a period of patient assessment, makes the reward more desirable, and more work is expended. This explanation is based upon the discrepancy perceived between small work and large amount of reward and is offered by the proponents of the theory of cognitive dissonance (Festinger, 1957). Another explanation is that frustration incurred from an inferred high drive level toward a goal brings about more effort, and another states that greater effort is simply more perceptually noticeable. The explanation suggested here is that greater effort is expended to match the behavior expected from an authority-object, and later as a part of the behavior of the work role. A small amount of money is meaningful only when the work is an approved social activity. Money later replaces social factors as a cue for the approval of work. The person is primarily aware of the self as a social object (Mead, 1934), and one's responses to others are governed by the object-to-object relationship. This reciprocity is most striking when one models his behavior and thoughts about himself against the behavior of another during work. Money is incidental as a reward unless it can be used in social transactions. The progression to a functionally autonomous (Allport, 1961) work role follows these steps: work-activity to approval or disapproval, to greater or less self-esteem, to source of approval perceived as authority about work, to authority perceived as behavioral model. Implicit in this formulation is that the self is an object, and that the change in self-image not only is cognitively based but takes in the liking or disliking of the new role. This formulation implies that adult behavior is still, perhaps more than we like to recognize, controlled by the continued approval of other persons we set up as models. This does not mean that we always like the models as persons, but that their approval or disapproval is important to our self-image.

The dependency that characterizes many of the transient unemployable members of our society can be used to benefit in working with them.

The process of rehabilitation we have described is a transitional phase and, as such, is similar to the work by Sears (1963) on the reinforcing role that permissiveness has for dependency. There is evidence showing that as the child grows, he is strongly motivated by dependency. Dependency is a pivotal personality trait in social role theory and may most aptly describe the relationship between the patient and role model, and the patient and the hospital as a whole, without casting the patient into the role of a child. Permissiveness from a benign authority characterizes to a considerable degree the psychological "climate" of the hospital/factory. It is still a hospital to most patients, and they recognize the authority of the role model. The staff of the hospital must remain in a sufficiently flexible but authoritative position to handle a variety of individual problems that are symptomatic of dependency.

Self-image and Personal Characteristics

Demographic characteristics, such as social status and age, determine the patient's enactment of the work role. A patient who is from a satisfying professional background will not respond to the role model of an unskilled worker. Marriage is a determining factor by which the patient finds the rationale for increasing his earning power in the hospital. These and other factors override, in some cases, the actual deviant behavior of the patient and the occasional antisocial behavior of the unemployable. Persons showing symptoms of mental disturbance that are not troublesome, but who have certain demographic characteristics such as having been married, may be placed outside the hospital.

The fact that such variables play a part in discharge from hospitals where the industrial workshop is less integrated into the hospital milieu has been documented (Query and Query, 1964). The variables have not been directly related to readmission, but remaining outside the hospital appears to be related to family expectations in cases where the patient is returning to the family unit (Freeman and Simmons, 1963). The factor of family expectations does not normally influence the staff's decision to advance the patient through the rehabilitation program. This is obviously true in cases where the staff know that family accommodation is no longer possible, and the patient concerned is found at a relatively high level of achievement.

Bennett and Wing (1963) have included re-education in the five functions they assign to the rehabilitation hospital. In special cases, the hospital can offer the patient resocialization opportunities in formal educational training. There has been considerable work accomplished in training subnormal adults and adolescents who have not necessarily been mentally ill, and who have not been institutionalized for long periods of time. Bringing such a program into the rehabilitation hospital, where it is sorely needed, creates special difficulties; one of these difficulties is the heterogeneous educational level of the adults prior to hospitalization. Another difficulty is utilizing the patient's time from the workshop. Other problems are incorporating the social education classes into the hospital ideology and placing the training instructors somewhere in the hospital hierarchy. The role of the instructor as a specific nursing role in the hospital described has been discussed by Skaeth (1964).

We formulated a theoretical basis for evaluating the hospital. Within this general framework, results of the studies must be considered exploratory in a novel environment. We must have answers to our questions before we can suggest a similar approach to areas other than rehabilitation of the chronic psychiatric patient. The questions are necessarily specific to the site of the research, and the conclusions are not to be generalized to all hospitals with rehabilitation programs. We must also remember that these studies were conducted in a rehabilitation hospital located in a rural setting with predominantly urban patients. The integration of the evaluation results and the answers we set down are applicable to all programs that would be set up in just the way and for the type of patient described in Chapter 2.

Patients who were successfully treated experienced changes in self-image along critical dimensions and in line with the overall image staff members had of them. There was a change in patients' perception of their status from predominantly mental patients to members of a select group of rehabilitees.[1] It was found that being mental patients still controlled many of their expectations. Among the entire staff, orientation was found to be more toward the patients than toward industrial production, and more toward their personal careers than toward the patients. These orientations varied systematically with circumstances of the organizational structure and one orientation (production) was associated with attitudes toward mental patients as a group. We assessed this attitude along the humanistic-custodial dimension. Association between custodialism and production did not appear inconsistent with the staff's shift toward an attitude of custodialism, because of the nature of the patient who appeared to achieve in the rehabilitation hospital setting and the ideology of the hospital in promoting this achievement.

Rehabilitation was described as a process requiring that the person begin to believe in a disposition of his case in the undetermined future. We found evidence of this process in the reference

---

[1] In the area of investigating how patients perceive themselves, Talbot and his associates, using the Osgood Semantic Differential Technique, found that psychotics and neurotics could be distinguished by their cognitions of what constituted their status. The psychotic patient viewed himself more as an infant and the neurotic saw himself higher on the development scale, that is, as an adolescent. Hospital-created positions and childlike activities were viewed. These investigators showed that hospital staffs can alter the perceived environment and that psychotics are able to discern this change (Talbot, *et al.*, 1961). It would seem that mental disturbance does not change perception of the external world, and that changes in the external world bring about internal changes in the self-concept, or in how the person perceives himself to be coping with that world.

group changes. We noted that the person must perceive himself as capable of carrying out this disposition. The self-image of "intelligence" increased; this increase suggests that this perceptual change occurs.

The following factors were found to determine progress in the environment: the achievers were found to be older, with diagnoses other than schizophrenic, and, if they were men, they were more likely to have been married. But if they were schizophrenic, the men also responded better than the women to the program. The young schizophrenic woman, consequently, was rare among the achievers. Early in their study, achievers showed rehabilitation promise by getting better work scores and by showing a greater ability to earn. The work scores, however, were highly susceptible to decrease because of their initial high level. These patients' assignments were changed relatively frequently despite the patients having been left more to their own devices.

The fact that many of the patients who were achieving in the hospital were not schizophrenic, and that a few had diffuse or focal brain damage, argues against the opinion of many rehabilitation workers that people with functional diagnoses are better risks. A revision of this notion seems to be in order. Working with the organically impaired person presents problems, such as matching the requirements of the job to the individual's impairment. This problem may take the form of matching the physical requirements of the procedure with the athetoid movements the individual may display, or matching certain memory requirements with an ability the individual may not possess. In any case, closer attention should be paid to the rehabilitation of the organic, since his potential has been underestimated.

We found that social education of the patients progresses in the rehabilitation hospital with many staff members taking part. Within the hospital's circumscribed program of social re-education, methods of presenting the material to be learned are not nearly as important as the mental condition of the patients in their ability to learn. Background factors play a part in separating those who benefit from the program from those who do not. A longer time in the hospital away from normal society affects retention, but does not affect the ability to learn. The person who has a shorter hospital experience both learns and retains the material.

The change in patient roles is markedly different from the change in staff roles. We will deal with both aspects in our discussion. The change in patient roles involves the rehabilitation process directly, or, in other words, the patient-staff interaction. The change in staff roles, on the other hand, involves an analysis of what the work in the rehabilitation hospital means in terms of new responsibilities, new spheres of activity, and new areas of training. Later, we will analyze in detail the roles of the psychologist and nurse, since the workers in these professions experience the greatest role change in the rehabilitation hospital structure.

Staff roles are established by authoritative decision and the ideology of the administration, but it is true that the enactment of the staff roles is also largely brought about by the patient-staff interactive process. It is only through discussions with patients about their work, for example, that the alert nurse recognizes what he or she can do to ease the problems that confront the patient. The nature of the patient who achieves, therefore, determines how the staff member interprets his role in the hospital community.

Patient Achievement and Staff Attitude

The combination of a high professional orientation, or the rewards professional status brings, with an emphasis on patient care places the staff member in the position of valuing, in patients, certain attributes more than others. People place a value on things that bring them professional satisfaction if they are oriented in a professional direction. The staff members tend to value those interpersonal characteristics of patients, such as intelligence and intelligent behavior (and also the patients who exhibit these qualities) which are viewed as means toward achieving the goal of a satisfying professional career, or, in this instance, the unique experience of rehabilitating long-term patients. It is perhaps inevitable that this feeling of professional satisfaction is transmitted to the patients more through the work role relationship than through the traditional helping role, where often it seems that nothing one does affects the chronicity of the disease. What is conceived to be intelligent behavior, whether tests show the patient to be natively intelligent or not, is valued by the staff member because it is necessary for rehabilitation to occur. The staff member creates, therefore, an atmosphere where he rewards intelligent behavior and the patient begins to construe that he, the patient, *is* intelligent through this process.[2] Support for this fact was obtained in the finding that one of the custodial scale items that changed toward a humanistic viewpoint (number 2 on page 232 in Appendix E) was related to patients' ability to discriminate right from wrong. We ultimately discover that "intelligent" is one trait that develops with time in the rehabilitation hospital as an ascribed self-image.

In order to sustain the work role relationship and bring about more professional rewards, the staff member very likely adopts a custodial point of view. The staff member, on this basis, arrives at the conviction that patients need more, not less, supervision, and that highly trained people, such as himself (professional orientation), are necessary to fulfill this need for supervision. These beliefs are augmented by the fact that the patients themselves tend to be chronic; two or three years are required for any perceptible change to occur. These beliefs are further reinforced by the staff members' observation that patients who respond to rehabilitation are older, having been initially hospitalized at an older age. Although the staff members may assume that these patients have been hospitalized for a longer period of time, our data do not support this assumption.

The type of patient and the manner in which he responds to rehabilitation influence the attitude of the staff. This influence depends where the staff member works in the hospital. Work roles in settings where the staff members are called upon to assess the patient as to either how much he produces or how he is functioning enhance the staff's patient orientation. Patient achievement in these situations is not as important to the rating of the patient's work as in those areas of the hospital where work roles are centered around productivity for the maintenance of the hospital industry. A higher

---

[2] *Intelligence* was one of the traits recognized by the role models as being desirable for rehabilitation. It was one on which the raters always agreed in their ratings of the patients (see page 80).

production orientation predominates among the staff in these areas where the emphasis is more on productivity than on assessment.

The nature of the staff-patient work role, therefore, alters as the patient progresses through the program. Shortly after he arrives, the patient is placed in the work role with staff people who show heightened individual patient involvement and professional interests. During the middle part of the patient's stay, the productivity aspect becomes more valued and the work role, with an emphasis on work, assumes greater importance. Near the time of his discharge and when he has proved himself to be productive, the patient is placed in a situation where the professional-patient-oriented relationship reverts to its former importance. This emphasis on professionalism is greater than that of patient-oriented individual assessment. This is as it should be, for it helps the patient's growing sense of confidence and lessens his anxiety about his role.

Self-image and Staff Attitude

The reader will recall that the long-stay patients who showed differences in various aspects of their self-images were workshop achievers. They were also achievers in terms of acquiring self-images thought to be necessary for rehabilitation by the role models. They were achievers in the sense of evaluating themselves in much the same way as the role models evaluated them. In addition, they achieved a greater certainty of what was expected of them and had fewer unrealistic expectations. The work role relationship, which the patient experienced through the attitudes of the staff, "traveled" through phases of professional to production to professional orientations, always with an overlay of a relatively high patient orientation. This progression resulted in a total benefit for the patient. In the area where the most regressed patients worked (among the workshops), productivity was not emphasized. It was shown how the factor of morale described in this chapter was dealt with by patient-oriented phases within the framework of the plan.

Change in self-image does not mean that patients become more and more positive toward their treatment (Reznikoff *et al.*, 1960). This change toward a positive outlook may occur within two years and six months after admission, as these investigators found; but, in the case of the rehabilitation hospital, where the patient has been hospitalized for many years, the patient's feelings and attitudes are complicated not only by the passage of time but by the introduction of an intensive work role experience. Our finding that reference group affiliation changed from mental patient toward member of the rehabilitation hospital suggests a positive commitment to rehabilitation.

We found that the patients focused more on their capacities and deficiencies in the work role and less on their feelings toward the hospital from which they came. This shift in attitude was gradual and came about only when the staff members showed greater concentration on production and the patients' contribution to it.

It is necessary, however, for a patient-oriented staff to convey to the patients their assets and liabilities during the assessment period. This period gives the patients some involvement in their own performance. This leads to greater discrimination of their performance on certain tasks and to a change in self-image. Interacting with role models and other staff members in group meetings, sports events, and group projects, such as the hospital magazine called *St. Wulstan's Weekly,* broadens their perception of their self-image to include other salient areas of human experience. It would appear that interacting with other female patients in a circumscribed group surrounded by the responsibilities of caring for homelike accommodations (the hostel) affects the sex self-image of even middle-aged patients. We did not explore further whether particular social attitudes were developed in this milieu among these patients. We have important evidence that environment changes self-image in this particular area in this period of life.

In general, the female patients were found to be more subject than men to a positive change in both self-image and personality traits despite the fact that, if they were schizophrenic, they did not do so well in terms of achievement. Among the changes noted on the test-retest of the same patients reported in Tables B-1 and B-2 in Appendix B, most of the changes were attributed to the women in the sample. The remarkable thing about these results is that the hospital is in no way designed to cater to feminine interests or in any predetermined way slanted toward an environment to bring about these particular changes. Yet twelve of the eighteen personality test scales showed a positive change for the women, and six of the eighteen for the men (see Table B-1).

It is quite possible that the reliability of the results from this test is much lower for patients of long-standing illness than for other people. In several cases, however, the results were in line with the self-image changes; this congruency showed a high level of reliability. The patients made great strides in finding a renewed self-confidence and optimism. These can be likened to *social presence* and *self-acceptance,* which for the men were among the few scales that increased. *Sociability* increased among the women but not among the men; *sociability* and *likable,* another increasing self-image, can be equated.

There are some conflicting results when the self-image and personality test data are compared. As a patient progresses through the hospital, for example, there is a decrease in his feeling of strength. There is some question as to whether the patients interpreted this self-image trait as mental or physical strength. If the predominant interpretation was mental, a case can be made for this change being mirrored in the data for *self-control,* which showed a marked decrease. On the other hand, the same can be said of *flexibility,* which also showed a decrease where an increase would be expected. If a patient felt that he was losing his "mental strength," he would tend to be more flexible, not more inflexible. The significant decrease in *absent-mindedness* suggests that a physical interpretation was made because both *strong* and *absent-mindedness* decreased. If *strong* was interpreted as being mental, these data would surely be inconsistent. The more common interpretation of physical strength is therefore more likely.

What factors in the staff attitude bring about these changes? An emphasis on production occurring as it does in the midpoint of the program, with an emphasis on profession occurring later, should produce many of these changes. We assume for a moment that the orientation of the staff affects to some significant degree the personality predispositions of the patients, and this assumption is consistent with the changes that we discovered. It will be remembered that the retested patients had been in the program for nine months. By this time most of the patients were in the middle unit. They had not experienced the higher professional orientation of the discharge unit staff. One specific personality test scale that could be linked meaningfully to this orientation, *capacity for status,* had not increased; it had, rather, decreased. The high production orientation of the staff members of the middle unit could have an impact on the differential results found between the sexes. The men patients in the sample would expect to perform better in the factory-like situation than the women, and frustration and a lowering of critical personality dimensions among the men would result when this challenge was not always met. This would be particularly true if these men were experiencing a tenuous change in sex role identification. A personality assessment of these men after they had been in the program for a longer period of time was not made. In this connection, it would appear that the women responded better than the men to the many group activities of the rehabilitation hospital with an increase in *sociability, tolerance,* and *ability to create a good impression.*

The assessment of self-image for three groups at different stages of rehabilitation enabled us to relate these changes to staff orientation. The elevated *anxious* and *hard-working* of the medium-stay group occurred in the unit where the staff's attitude was directed primarily toward production. These images are consistent with production pressure. The self-image of these medium-stay patients toward being slow can also be explained in the same fashion —that is, a constant push toward meeting production deadlines would make this self-image more meaningful, more perceptible to others, and, therefore, more within the person's awareness. It would require some yardstick such as productive capacity to meet the orientation of the staff to measure one's slowness on the job. An increase in *anxious* as a patient self-image appears to be associated with a production orientation on the part of the staff. The traits of *strong, hard-working, optimistic,* and *slow* showed relatively high agreement, and, therefore, were highly perceptible among the staff members. This finding further suggests that these particular self-images are more suspectible to change through social interaction around a work role than others. Only those traits *slow* and *hard-working,* which serve to directly gauge and influence productivity, altered with the medium-stay group, in contrast to the long- and short-stay groups. We can conclude that those patient self-images that are dependent upon production flow change with a shift in staff attitude, and that a shift in attitude brings about direct changes in how the patients perceive themselves in relation to the work.

✌ SELF-IMAGE AND INSTITUTIONAL STRUCTURE ໄ

So as not to lose sight of the main thesis—that self-image depends upon institutional structure—it is appropriate to repeat here that these changes can only come about when, to use Jules Henry's terms (1957), the staffing of the hospital is a "unified system" rather than the usual "multi-differentiated system." The self-image change results from the ongoing interaction between patients and the same role models in both living and working situations. Where there is a system of coordinating areas of responsibility between two or more groups of professionals in a multi-differentiated hospital, such as between ward nurses and industrial therapists, and where there are present the conflicting views of the patient that can accrue from this system, a positive change of self-image is much more difficult for the patient to experience. The fact that in a unified system differing staff orientations and self-image changes can be related so closely and logically to one another is evidence of the relationship between the institution's structure and the self-perceptions of the people who live there. Finding personality changes in a unified system suggests even more the relationship between structure and inmate, and requires more study in hospitals where role models and work role relationships are not present.

The unified system differs from the multi-differentiated system in significant ways. The differences in the way patients perceive various roles of members of the staff in the multi-differentiated mental hospital are known by most workers in such hospitals. The doctor, as a "distant" authority, is looked upon as a source of medical knowledge but rarely as the person who gives orders affecting the patients. The orders are carried out by nursing assistants and nurses, and it is with these people that the patient has daily contact. These staff members are seen as the source of comfort or discomfort to the patient, and orders emanate from them. The nurse is seen as a dispenser of medicine and advice and as the person who sees that the patient manages to maintain a clean appearance. The closest interpersonal relationship between the patient and a member of the staff is often reserved for the nursing assistant. This poses a problem to the patient who, by reason of education and self-image, relates poorly to nursing assistants.

All too often the patient grows to believe that he is an object to those who exercise the most authority and those with the greatest training and expertise about his welfare. The trend in our society in this general direction was discussed in Chapter 2. This tendency is seen in its most vivid way in conducting hospital rounds, particularly on a crowded mental hospital ward among ambulatory patients.

In contrast to the multi-differentiated system, the unified system places the nurse in a central position of significant interaction with the patient. The frequent meetings with the doctor bring him, with his perceived authority, into interaction with the patient in the company of the nurse, who will be delegated to carry out the decisions, and the assistants and orderlies, who have the closest interaction with the patients.

Reference Group and Staff Attitude

The dominant group that determines the patient's thinking about himself or his reference group alters during rehabilitation. At this point, let us review the findings regarding reference group affiliation. The change is brought about to the extent that the long-stay resident in the hospital maintains, to some extent, the mental hospital identity in addition to a new-found rehabilitation hospital identity. He is also more emphatically aware of what is expected of him and, as a group, these patients are more homogeneous in having fewer unrealistic aspirations than newly admitted patients have.

The staff's consistently held patient orientation may explain why the patient keeps the mental patient reference group throughout much of his hospitalization. If the staff members continually see the patient as a more important aspect of their work than other considerations, the patient role is reaffirmed at every stage in the interaction that is carried on between them and the patient. (The patient is continually evaluated in the review committee meetings in all work areas, for example.) This patient-oriented interaction serves to bring reality more into focus for the patient, particularly in the vocational area. A self-image of greater confidence and optimism is reflected in the "washing out" of unrealistic expectations toward the termination of the patient's stay. The patient orientation of the intake unit staff is not as high as the other staff units and, of course, the interaction is only in its beginning stages, so that one does not find an immediate change in the patient's reference group or self-image.

Achievement in the hospital program is independent of how young the patient is, and the evidence suggests that the older, achieving patient is able to change his reference group, or at least adopt a new one, as easily as the younger patient. The "chronicity hypothesis," holding that a period of unremitting illness is necessary for change to occur in the patient, states nothing about the factors that impinge on the patient to bring this change about. One of these factors may well be a set of circumstances—a transfer, for example —that makes it possible for the patient to identify with another institution or group of persons. Whether this occurs in any transfer or whether the new environment should be like the one we have described is still an open question.[3]

Evidence shows that patients who achieve in the rehabilitation hospital are somehow able to form friendships with other patients from the same parent hospital. The fact that the achievers were more rarely schizophrenic most certainly has much to do with the fact that friendships were formed and sometimes resulted in

---

[3] I have emphasized parts of the environment, such as the workshops, to the exclusion of other features; this tendency may have influenced my thinking. There has been a tendency to equate the units with the workshops. In actual fact, the patients spend a small amount of their waking day in the workshops and the changes found may be in part the result of social interaction that goes on elsewhere, in addition to the work.

multiple living arrangements with these friends after discharge. This does not mean that friendships are impossible for schizophrenics, but that friendships leading to sharing an apartment are unlikely among the chronically withdrawn. Despite the fact that their assignments and jobs were frequently changed (or because of this fact), the achievers were able to rate themselves more confident and intelligent to handle these jobs.

The notable influence of socioeconomic class as a reference group on preference of treatment and the relationship between therapist and patient that has been demonstrated so convincingly (Hollingshead and Redlich, 1958) was not shown in the field of rehabilitation as practiced in this hospital. It might be true that some nurses preferred working with patients from particular social classes, or those they "liked." It might be that patients with particular characteristics tend to become more involved in the Social Committee and such. It appears that diagnosis and level of education, and perhaps intelligence, outweigh socioeconomic factors. As far as socioeconomic factors are related to the other factors named, they would determine a given patient's career in the hospital program. Achievement cuts across all socioeconomic levels, at least among those represented (there were no Class I patients among those studied).

❧ SOCIAL RE-EDUCATION AND THE RESULTS ❧

In analyzing the social re-education classes, we found that a program of formal social re-education was beneficial and that it had a valuable place in the hospital program. It was more beneficial for some patients than for others, and for patients in some units more than others. There is a possibility, for example, that staff orientation may influence patient participation. There was a hint of this in the finding that the lowest overall learning among the patients in the social re-education classes occurred with those patients from the unit whose staff held the highest production orientation. This conclusion is mitigated, however, upon closer inspection of all of the units. Comparing the mean increases for the patients from different units on page 250 in Appendix G with the staff orientations in Table E-2, we find an inverse correspondence between the two factors, staff with the high patient and production orientations, and patients with low increase in test scores. The profession orientation appears unrelated to these score changes.

Many other factors are involved in patients' being able to learn from the program, but the way in which role models on the units and elsewhere interpret the program in discussing it with the patients is bound to engender some feeling toward the social re-education classes. It is possible that some patients felt that it was an undue interference with their work (although they were reimbursed for their attendance), and furthermore, that it would take them away from the relationship between themselves and the role models. The first situation would explain the relationship between lack of test score increases and high production orientation. The second situation would explain the relationship between lack of test score increases and high production orientation. The second situation would explain the relationship between high patient orientation and lack of the score increases. If these perceptions of the classes were true to any degree, it is possible that learning in the classes would be affected and our result would not be so strange for these motivational reasons. The hiatus between what transpires in the workshops and in the social re-education program may be less real than apparent.

Giving a place in the review committee meetings to the psychologist and the instructor, where planning of the patient's program is done, introduces the existence of the program and those involved in it to the patient early in his treatment. The mysterious aspect of the program, which may follow a vague reference to it while the patients are being escorted around the hospital grounds in a group after they arrive, is lessened and the program becomes a meaningful part of the hospital structure for them. This aspect of the program— giving a place to the instructors in the review meetings—should be retained in such a hospital/factory if it were set up to rehabilitate other groups, such as the poverty victims.

In a lesser sense of the term, the social re-education personnel serve as role models to the patients assigned to the classes. They act as tutors except where the physical training of the patients is concerned. Where physical training is involved, attention is focused on the patient's motility and customary gait. Patients sometimes exhibit ways of walking (due in part to medication) and physical lethargy that make them conspicuous in the community. The rehabilitation hospital staff believe that a change in this area, along with emphasis on personal grooming, is necessary for complete merging with the world outside the hospital, and for a change in self-image.

Ideally, of course, the patient should retain his self-image of individuality and it is very unrealistic to think that this will not occur to a significant extent. Individuality and idiosyncratic behavior patterns are different concepts; one is socially adaptive, and the other, tending to be eccentric, is not. In any case, one does not wish the patient to become an asocial nonentity, but to contribute in his own way to the society in which he finds himself, rather than being fearful of it or being a burden to it.

There are problems unique to a program of re-education in physical activity in the rehabilitation hospital or hospital/factory. The hospital staff has not found an effective way of working out these problems beyond assigning the patients to groups for team participation in sports-like activities and taking them from their work during the time the classes are held. Calisthenics are employed wherever necessary. It is possible that the self-image changes that were found were related to these activities. Not all patients are assigned to these groups, but among those long-stay patients who marked themselves as being *slow*, 68 per cent had participated in the groups at one time or another. These results are only suggestive. They demonstrate, however, that activities other than work can produce self-image change along dimensions highly related to the activity.

⋙ ROLES OF THE STAFF: THE NURSE ⋘

We studied in the evaluation a large group of nurses in terms of how they perceived their job in the rehabilitation hospital and how certain attitudes affected the patients under their care. The job requirements of the rehabilitation environment place the nurse in a novel relationship with the patient, and we have substantiated that this relationship is pedagogic in a subtle way.

The results of the study suggest that the growing emphasis on rehabilitation in hospitals will produce a custodial point of view in many nursing quarters. The usual belief that custodialism is somehow "bad" and humanistic ideas are innately "good" is questionable when rehabilitation is attached meaningfully to the requirements of keeping the patient in custody. The change in role that the nurses and manual arts therapists will experience, and which they will find is temporarily custodial (as defined by the critical statements on page 232 in Appendix E), is not contradictory with the mission of the hospital. The nurse will feel much less guilt if this fact—perhaps as a rationalization—is recognized.

Our finding that in-service training is important for the nurse's image, and, above all, to the nurses' ability to understand their patients, is indicative of an uncertainty of role. A change of role, perhaps toward the one of a role model in which the nurses find themselves in the rehabilitation hospital, will help this flagging image. The question, for example, of whether to wear a clean, white uniform or not will be resolved out of necessity when the nurse works with the patient on dirty equipment.

A definition of the role of nurse as a work role at the outset of her orientation would offer the nurse a basis on which to find satisfaction in what she is doing. It would further differentiate the psychiatric nursing role from the role of the nurse in general practice, although, as with the psychologist, psychiatric problems are only one set of possibilities for which this approach or rehabilitation is appropriate.

One of the most relevant studies to our discussion of the self-image of nurses was done by Benne and Bennis (1959). They found that (1) there was very little agreement between the things nurses desired in their work and the rewards the hospitals were able to offer, and (2) what the nurses valued was not under supervisory control. The nursing ideal was to spend less time with administrative matters, such as the writing of records, than they actually do. We found, for example, the following distribution to the statement: "I would be very unhappy to find myself so involved with administration that I would lose all patient contact." ($N = 31$)

3%	10%	13%	26%	48%
Strongly Disagree	Moderately Disagree	Neutral	Moderately Agree	Strongly Agree

With this approach, rehabilitation administration—in the practical sense of maintaining staff morale while working with the products in a hospital—is probably more important than guaranteeing adequate coverage of the units. In addition, the hospital is structured in such a way that the nursing administrators themselves have almost daily contact with patients in carrying out their supervisory tasks.

Benne and Bennis (1959) found that most nurses choose nursing for practical reasons rather than for the "ideal" image of service that the role conveys. These results are consistent with the relatively high professional orientation that we found, although care of patients was higher, but not significantly so. The fact that nurses may work with patients in an industrial setting in the approach described here does not alter the dominant professional feelings of the nurses themselves.

The approach to patient care has the potential of altering the situation found by these investigators (Benne and Bennis, 1959) in that rewards (such as direct and constant contact with patients) are under the direct control of the supervisory staff. These supervisors also share many of the nurses' biases and beliefs about the patients and the hospital. Nurses can participate in the formulation of policy through representation to the Policy Committee. For the many who enter nursing for practical reasons, the help they give patients in finding a satisfying work experience vicariously fulfills these practical needs. Less time is spent in writing about discussions with patients and keeping discursive records, such as medicine changes and their effects, and these notations are substituted by more meaningful checklists of the patients' performance on the jobs.

There are many settings where nurses as role models can work despite the growing shortage of trained nurses and other professional people. It is hoped that the challenge of this approach to rehabilitation will bring more workers into the field because of its promise. The data we gathered suggest that professional nurses acquainted with the problem of the unemployed—particularly the unemployed chronic mental patient—are enthusiastic with this type of approach.

◆§ ROLES OF THE STAFF: THE PSYCHOLOGIST §◆

Mention has been made of the fact that pedagogic functions also befall the psychologist when he works in a hospital devoted to the rehabilitation potential of patients. This trend is consistent with a change in the nature of psychotherapy over the past decade that has been observed by such reviewers of the field as Stieper and Wiener (1965). They discuss the behavioristic influence on therapy as emphasizing the teaching of adaptive behavior. The psychologist may become a "social" teacher both in the hospital and in the university classroom. This does not imply a derogation of the psychologist's traditional role of therapist and psychological exam-iner, but gives a new dimension to his clinical profession.

As psychologists become more and more involved in counsel-ing with welfare programs, teaching clients not only for what sort of employment they have an aptitude after the appropriate tests have been administered, but instructing them in the ways of behaving on the job and the rudimentary things they need to know in con-nection with their jobs, such as filling out forms for employment benefits and such, will become necessary. Many of these training programs will be conducted according to operant conditioning prin-ciples. This trend can only make the counseling psychologist's job more rewarding, interesting—and demanding.

A greater involvement in the routine of the hospital work program will be required of the psychologist as he coordinates his activities with those of the work groups. He will continue to be called upon to detach himself from his office and to explore, with other staff members and patients, the possibilities of satisfactory rehabili-tative relationships in the community. The variety of community-oriented functions of the psychologist have increased (Libo, 1966), and the introduction of a social re-education program will in a sense revert the psychologist's interest back to the institution. One can only hope that more clinical psychologists will become socially responsive to the need of "rehabilitating" institutions by establishing such programs.

The most pressing problem in psychotherapy—and the factor that is lacking among those whose need for "social" therapy is the greatest: the sociopath, the psychotic, and the underprivileged —is motivation. Psychologists are well aware of this, and have devoted a vast amount of effort in analyzing the experimental basis of motivation. Unfortunately, these experiments have not been directed toward those populations served by rehabilitation hospitals. Exceptions to this are the experiments on the rewards of work. Some of the aspects of monetary motivation as an effortful activity as it applied to the rehabilitation hospital were explored in this chapter.

The psychologist's role in the rehabilitation hospital as an expert in the techniques of motivating people is crucial, and he interprets the knowledge of the factors and the standing of the theories that are current to other members of the staff in their work. The insights gained from these experiments can be applied to the hospital program. In this sense the hospital program is always in a state of flux and evaluation.

It is not solely within the context of social re-education that the psychologist can be of service. Only by broadening his perspective to the hospital as a microcosm community can he appreciate the forces at his disposal. He can knit together these forces in routine appraisals of staff and patient morale and relations with the outside community. It is well to remember that the sort of patient he and the other personnel are treating is rarely eager for rehabilitation despite some stating vaguely that they have "come to be rehabilitated." This lack of motivation is often prominent among the poor, owing to their past experiences with the unfulfilled promises of education.

The future role of the psychologist, as it pertains to the rehabilitation effort, will necessitate a much more catholic point of view. The trend toward specialization so apparent and sometimes so condemned by practicing psychologists will be reversed. The role demands will require the psychologist to possess a more-than-nodding acquaintance with principles in social, educational, and experimental psychology, although his identity as a clinical psychologist or a counseling psychologist may remain intact.

The fact that the hospital described here rehabilitated the long-term mental patient is incidental to the basic role of the psychologist. Rehabilitation of prisoners in a work program, similar to the one described, will require certain knowledge, and in this sense, specialization of one type of inmate rather than another will be needed. The actual techniques of the discipline, whether they be from social psychology or industrial psychology, will serve the psychologist working in such settings. Whether he will be known as just "psychologist," or "a rehabilitation psychologist," or the "psychologist whose major interest is rehabilitating people" is premature and probably unnecessary. What is necessary are the elements of curiosity (how far can one go with certain types of people in rehabilitation?), compassion (empathic understanding of the distress resulting from the process of rehabilitation of the person), and doubt (not anticipating full rehabilitation following a partial success) enunciated by Bordin (1966).

In the next chapter we shall concern ourselves with the very wide applications of such a plan. Is it equally applicable not only to persons who have found themselves in a sick role but to any group of persons who are ostensibly uneducable, who are wasted, and who are marginal to an increasingly mechanized and specialized society? We sincerely believe that it is. We will transfer our concrete example of the rehabilitation hospital concept to other analogous programs for the future and to those that are currently operating or are being planned for American communities.

EIGHT

Wider Applications

The material contained in these chapters (and indeed in many books that have been written concerning work) has been presented from the middle-class American or at least Western point of view. This perspective is necessary for a discussion of poverty in our own society. We set forth as one of our objectives in the first chapter of this book a discussion of poverty in all societies. In this concluding chapter, we will describe the general aspects of poverty. We will preface this discussion with some remarks regarding broad generalizations because, as has been pointed out previously, extrapolation from rehabilitation programs for mental patients in Western society to the poverty of man is not a "leap" but a "bound" in our thinking. However, there is reason to believe that work holds significance for all people as surely as does poverty in mind and body.

An occasional author writing about work broadens his perspective and considers work as a "way of life" or a "social act" (Borow, 1964). This does not mean that men must work, nor even that men can only realize a satisfying life through work, be it the creativity of the aboriginal sand-artist or the productivity of the lathe operator. Work as a "social act" means that men interact significantly with others, and in so doing, they ward off alienation among themselves and the definition of themselves and their lives as useless that comes about from not finding work to do.

The ideas of one's society and self-image that result from work, therefore, become the mirror images, or the opposites, of the ideas and images that result from not working.

It is still difficult to grasp the momentous implications of the effect of work as a human activity unless we amend the statement that men work to protect themselves from alienation to say that men strive purposefully for the interpersonal encounters provided by working, unless they are thwarted.[1] Purposive striving prevails until the erosive effects of poverty (or being institutionalized for a chronic mental disability) halt, or at least interrupt, the process of striving. The point of view expressed here, which we have held consistently throughout this book, is that positive striving is an end, not a means, and is circumscribed at least in part by the image the person has of himself. The vehicle by which this striving takes place is often social modeling. Self-image, or self-esteem, is, therefore, one of the more potent indices of mental health. Kornhauser (1965) has shown this among the employed factory workers. It is also one of the most effective indices of rehabilitation among the unemployed, as we have shown in our evaluation of the hospital/factory.

The fact that less than satisfactory self-images, and, more pervasively, less than satisfactory images of others and society in general, characterizes the employed factory worker is also shown in Kornhauser's analysis. Over half of the men he studied, for example, were pessimistic about their immediate future (Kornhauser, 1965, p. 47). This state of affairs can be partly explained by the alienation between people that we have discussed in the opening pages of Chapter 2. We have evidence, therefore, that industrial work itself does not lead to self-satisfaction, particularly for the ordinary semi-skilled worker. In the hospital/factory approach, both the role model relationship and the group discussions amid repetitive work serve to make the work situation different from the work

---

[1] A similar view of motivation can be found in psychotherapeutic writings such as Singer's (Singer, 1965) and is implied in the work of personality theorists which Singer discussed. These theorists do not ascribe to the tension-reduction conceptualization of motivation.

situation in those jobs analyzed by this investigator and others who have analyzed work relationships (Kahn *et al.,* 1964).

There is one population characteristic in both of the above data sources (Kornhauser's and our own) that upon reflection makes broad and sweeping generalizations difficult. This is the matter of race. In both studies only white persons were used (there were no other racial groups represented in the rehabilitation hospital). We do not have evidence to show that race is an exception to the theory. We must recognize, however, that among the populations where poverty abounds, races other than white probably predominate, and before our theoretical assumptions are completely validated this problem must be resolved empirically. This would be especially true of cross-racial modeling.

One concept that relates to work irrespective of race and culture, and which has profound importance in the study of personality, is competence (White, 1959). Taking our cue from the fact that one of the psychological features of the hospital/factory is the self-image of competence that the staff shows the patient, we can further extend our theoretical approach and the ideology of the institution to other cultures by an analysis of human competence.

✑§ COMPETENCE THROUGH WORK ROLE INTERACTION ৡ❧

In Chapter 6, we noted that psychologists have paid relatively little attention to volition as a concept in rehabilitation. Our experience with institutionalized people has shown us that volition is a key concept and is related to the person's image not only of himself but of the institution, and, perhaps more crucially, to the society of which he is a part.

We have further found that self-image alters through purposeful activity such as work. Without an empirical basis, we submit that work has meaning for the vast majority, and that unemployment affects the subjective influence that a person believes he has on other people. This is the basis of the psychology of poverty: the loss of interpersonal competence.

It is from White's analysis of competence that we are able to understand some of the results that were found in the evaluation of the hospital/factory (White, 1959). One example may suffice: the fact that the older patient achieved so outstandingly, while the young and older schizophrenic achieved less, suggests that the former person had the ability to act in such a way as to achieve an interpersonal effect. According to White's formulation, competence can partly be measured by intelligence and aptitude. More importantly, it can be tapped subjectively as a "sense," effective through projective personality tests, such as the Thematic Apperception Test. The subject indicates a preference for stories in which people achieve desired effects by word and action. For our purposes, White has expressed the loss of this sense most cogently in his analysis of schizophrenia as a final surrender of this sense. This "surrender" is based in turn upon a "chronic weakness" of the sense of being competent (White, 1966).[2] He continues by linking this concept to material about childhood training and the interactional effects between parent and child.

In another direction, we suggest that a sense of competence as a self-image (being "confident" and "intelligent" and having fewer unrealistic aspirations) can be acquired through the interactional effects of a role model. In our example (the hospital/factory), the modeling took the form of being competent in doing an assigned job or task. Working on objects together was the basis of the relationship, "objects" in this context being the toys packaged, or even the entire contract with an outside manufacturer.

A sense of competence regarding objects is readily extended to a sense of interpersonal competence, especially in the work relationship formed at the hospital/factory. It is important to note that even in the "clinic" (see Chapter 3), interpersonal competence is emphasized with its group projects and shared experiences with the staff.

Competence, therefore, is the subjective belief that, despite

[2] Extending this concept to the poverty-ridden does not imply any such "weakness," constitutional or otherwise. The "weakness" may, however, be a significant result of poverty.

material poverty, one is able to influence the beliefs and actions of others. This does not mean "creating an impression" in the ordinary meaning of becoming a desired object to the observer. (The poverty victim may certainly create an impression of undesirability.) Rather, it means that what one says and does "counts" in some subtle way in interpersonal interaction. It also does not mean "being an expert," for many experts fail in conceiving of themselves as being influential.

Competence in work is one of the most significant attributes common to all cultures. Competence in sexual relationships is another. The forms taken and the outlets of both are dependent upon features of the culture and, as White suggests, are dependent upon childhood experiences and, we submit, upon the experiences beyond.

Placing competence within the context of social pressures means not only that it is outside psychopathology, but also that it is reversible. We have preferred to use the phrase "role model relationship" in our conceptualization. We found that changes are brought about among people whose lives are psychopathological in nature. Competence was found to be amenable to pressure irrespective of the extent of mental disturbance, and we believe that this comes about primarily if not exclusively through work. We have found that changes of attitude and perspective also occur among those who work with them—the staff. These are not psychopathological people, but changes nevertheless occurred. We do not know if these changes were in the direction of more competence, but observing the members of the staff in their daily tasks, we were impressed by their confidence in influencing the patients. This is a question, however, that as yet remains unanswered. It may well be that in order to be an effective role model, competence, as White defines it, must change in accordance with the other person's self-image, and the relationship is truly an interaction.

Several other theoretical and practical questions remain beyond the obvious one of whether such an approach as this one will affect normal but poor individuals of the same age in the same way. Before discussing the practical applications of this approach in other fields there are some questions left unanswered: Is work necessarily a social act? As an example, consider the composer working in isolation. In other words, is the product itself a social act? Does recognition affect the self-image?

Does the objective measurement of self-image as used in this evaluation reflect the subjective sense of competence?

What are the characteristics of an effective role model? Are they the same for the mental patient as for the poverty victim?

Do morale factors, such as reasonable pay, affect the modeling process?

Finally, is there indeed a relationship, as implied in the opening pages of Chapter 2, between the national self-image and the extent and character of poverty in a particular country?

◄§ EXTENSION OF THE APPROACH §►

The personal anomie and psychodynamic effects of chronic unemployment that shadow the lives of some members of American society today were briefly reviewed in Chapter 2. A tragically large and growing number of potentially salvageable people are discovering that they no longer fit into the social order. They have neither the skills nor the incentive to cope with the complexities of modern life. They are going their various ways alone and disheartened and finding individual means of escape. On rare occasions they strike out in violence against the society—against an empty landscape that is threatening to absorb them into its emptiness. But it cannot be concluded with assurance that they have given up certain basic needs when, in some cases, an acquisitive society such as ours makes these needs even more than normally attractive.

Encouraging these people to take up a meaningful work role is one of the hitherto unexplored ways of restructuring their lives and relationships with others, as well as of redeeming their damaged opinion of themselves. The poverty victim's relationship with society is a dependent one, impersonal and often degrading. The role models closest to these people are others who are burdened by the same anxieties about sheer existence, or they are, for many people, figures of authority, such as policemen, ministers, and social workers, who are placed in special categories of interpersonal relationships. The establishment of an environment of productivity for these people, where the authority is structured in the work role, fills certain psychological and social as well as material needs and liberates these people from the economy of the country as paupers.

The ultimate in social responsibility is the severing of this dependency bond between man and the state in a way similar to that of the child serving its own identity from the identity of its mother.

We will take up the analysis begun in the first chapter of this book, of the poverty situation as it exists in the United States today.

In her book *The Psychology of Occupations* (1956), Anne Roe related Maslow's need system to the motivation to work and concluded that having an occupation was potentially the most fruitful way to fulfill these various needs at all levels (from "physiological" through "need for esteem" to the "need for self-actualization"). If this is the case, a loss more staggering than the mere percentage of unemployed and the resulting national disgrace is being perpetuated by the failure to deal with the problem of unemployment. The cumulative drain of need fulfillment is incalculable if one subscribes to this theory, and, even if one does not classify occupation as a primary need satisfier, the association between the incidence of physical and mental illness and unemployment suggests a gigantic loss to society in the health of its members (Faris and Dunham, 1939; Leighton *et al.*, 1963).

Apart from the group with no income at all, people with low incomes have irregular hours, no sick leave, and few resources for treatment of their illnesses. Their financial situation creates special problems of the kind of treatment that can be made available to them (Riessman *et al.*, 1966). For the treatment of mental disorder, not only is lengthy analysis often suspect and too expensive for the impoverished person, but shock treatments and drug therapy, the usual modes of treatment for poor people, are poorly chosen if we wish to maintain the patient's marginal income and need satisfaction through his recovery. Recuperation is a period when productivity is important not only for its psychiatric benefits but also for its economic ones, especially if the patient is a father and husband. Loss of income, however, is only part of the problem of the low income person. He is enmeshed in a society that is outstanding for its glittering materialism; his self-image is an image of a person who cannot share in the glitter. He is in a society where centralization has created "personnel pyramids" and has regimented interpersonal relationships in a system poorly equipped to help him.

The Unemployed in America

The incongruity between the presence of a large number of unemployed and the affluence of the American society that surrounds them has recently attracted the notice of many social scientists (Fishman, 1966; Gordon, 1966; Will and Vatter, 1964; Miller, 1966; Meissner, 1966; Harrington, 1964). The avalanche of books on this topic gives us an idea of the number of searching analyses into the causes of this phenomenon. Many of these analyses emphasize the interrelated nature of the social structure in making the problem nationwide. The presence of a distressed minority can influence more than one community because of the interdependence of communities. Sufrin and Buck (1963), for example, found that chronic underdevelopment and unemployment was dependent upon the business not of one firm but of many. Before suggesting how the hospital/factory approach can help ease the situation, we should identify the chronically unemployed in this country.

Despite our reservations about statistics on the grounds that they depersonalize the poverty victim, discussing a few statistical points is helpful. W. H. Franke (1965) has presented a review of the current problem. He defines the hard-core, long-term unemployed as those persons who have been out of work for fifteen successive weeks or more. Immediately a contrast between the chronic unemployed and the mental patients discussed in this book is demonstrated. The average length of hospitalization (and unemployment) of these patients was twelve years, and they were probably out of work several months before first being hospitalized. This period of idleness is approximately forty times as long as that of the chronically unemployed. There are, however, some similarities between the two populations. In our analysis, the married man was found to be the better "risk" for the hospital program. The approximate incidence of married patients in the rehabilitation hospital was 25 per cent. Of the chronically unemployed, 33.9 per cent are married men (Franke, 1965). The similarity of these data suggests that many of these chronically unemployed people would achieve in a similar program. Approximately one half of the rest of the chronically unemployed group (single men, 31.8 per cent, and all women, 15–20 per cent) receive public and private assistance. Of the married men, one third have a wife who is working and a half have some other member of the family who is earning. This percentage of working wives is approximately the same as for the married male mental patient group that we studied. It is possible to generalize our findings of achievement in the program to the poverty victim on the basis of marriage, although the populations are notably different in terms of years of unemployment.

Statistics indicate that the hard-core element of unemployment is increasing. In June, 1964, it comprised 34.6 per cent of the unemployed and in December of that year, 46.1 per cent (*Occupational Outlook Quarterly,* 1966). Seasonal fluctuations have less influence on these figures than the number of people seeking their first job have.

The fact that the economy of the region is a factor, but not as great a one as commonly believed, is suggested by the finding that one fifth of the unemployed are found in depressed areas where few jobs are to be found. Not all of these people, however, are long-term unemployed. In labor-surplus areas, the unemployed are older, as one would expect, and they are more than likely to have been in some sort of factory work (Franke, 1965).

The slow "silting" of the chronically unemployed, and therefore the growth of poverty surrounded by affluence, is due in part to two facts: (1) the rates of long-term unemployment fail to decrease as fast as the national output increases during periods of economic recovery; (2) the "long-term" category comprises a greater proportion of the total unemployment in each successive period of prosperity. A part of these phenomena can be ascribed to the erosion of confidence and ineptness in finding work that long-term unemployment brings about. As success produces more success, the span between the unsuccessful and the successful widens and more disadvantaged people observe this gulf with growing disillusionment.

Automated industry has also played a part in the first observation pertaining to the increase of national output. Our analysis of the rehabilitation hospital approach and its implications in correcting the effects of unemployment is more directly concerned with the latter phenomenon, that is, the rise of the members of the "long-term" category even during prosperous years.

Although all categories of workers suffer from long-term unemployment (and, in connection with this point, we found that most classes of workers were represented in the achieving patients of the rehabilitation hospital), there are three types of workers who tend to become long-term problems: (1) the young workers, non-white, who are blue collar in the sense of being semi-skilled operatives and unskilled laborers; (2) somewhat older workers whose last employment was in the goods-producing industries (particularly durable goods such as manufacturing, mining, and construction); (3) the new entrants into the labor force who are teen-agers with minimal education and are searching for their first job (Franke, 1965). Many of those in the last group are the school "dropouts," whose outlook on education is dismal, to say the least.

These categories tend to be restricted to men, but in many cases these men go on to marry and their wives assume the responsibility of working when the situation deteriorates for them to this extent. Other men marry women who are working at the time of the marriage and a role reversal is already formed if the men do not also find employment.

The attitude toward types of work may influence the incidence of unemployment. Many members of the families of the unemployed expect that the children will work as soon as they are physically able to do so, and manual work, such as farming and manufacturing, is the only type of occupation that they classify as "real work." The domestic service occupations, except porters, caretakers, housekeepers in hospitals, are filled largely by women and shunned by men. In connection with this point, some male mental patients who perform hospital housekeeping assignments might do well in these household occupations. Some jobs, therefore, are not sought by the disadvantaged because of prevailing attitudes among the potential workers themselves.

All of these groups (both those who have lost jobs and those who have never had one but are looking for work) require considerable guidance, counseling, and, above all, a person or persons with whom to relate while performing to their capacity on rewarding tasks. The approach to rehabilitation through a structured environment fulfills many of these prerequisites, renders sociotherapy, and alleviates economic deprivation.

The rehabilitation plan is, basically, a free enterprise form of work relief. Recent public support for work relief rather than fiscal maneuvers to combat unemployment has been due to a renewed interest in the gross national product (Freeman, 1965). Work relief appears to be more flexible in the scheduling of work to be done and holds the most promise of reaching the growing number of unemployed.

For several reasons, the approach of the rehabilitation hospital is admirably suited to the needs of the unemployed with the least skills. It could be assimilated into such programs as the Job Corps, where training the "uneducable" is sometimes necessary to keep the person of very low intellect from criminal behavior as a livelihood as well as to provide a diversion from his plight. The Job Corps, in its diversity of education and work, is very similar to this approach but, of course, is slanted toward the problems of the young male of minority group status.

First of all, the rehabilitation hospital plan permits the role model concept to function with a minimum of bureaucratic interference. The line of authority does not extend beyond the immediate environment of the rehabilitees. The rehabilitees, called Corpsmen or enrollees in the Job Corps, share with the models those social amenities, such as sports activities and club membership, that are established and, to a large extent, the rehabilitees can model their behavior in these organizations on the conduct of the staff in like situations. This aspect is found in some Job Corps Centers and not in others, and in those that have this aspect the age difference between the training personnel and the enrollees may pose problems of identification.

Secondly, in the rehabilitation hospital approach, guidance

and counseling are given where they are most useful at regular periodic intervals—on the job. Guidance is an integral part of the work flow; the eruption of feelings of frustration, growing out of unemployment, and feelings of being "untrainable," which threaten the rehabilitee's mental stability, can be channeled into the group discussions.

Thirdly, dependence upon public funds is sharply decreased because of the self-supporting nature of the rehabilitation hospital. Public funds are sometimes more difficult to solicit for people who are believed to be beyond training in the ordinary, formal way. This is probably even more true of the older transient than of the younger Job Corpsman. This factor of financial independence also frees the organization from a certain amount of bureaucratic influence attached to the expenditure of state and national budgets and gives the entire staff and personnel an autonomy rarely found in such programs.

Training in savings and job interviews go hand-in-hand with the progress of the work. The temptation of "spree" buying and conspicuous consumption among those who have been unrewarded for a long time can be handled with understanding within the framework of the organization.

Lastly, the physical disabilities of older people that are often exacerbated by chronic unemployment and poverty can be treated through the clinic, which is a part of, and yet separate from, the work areas.

As it is now structured, the Job Corps, as a method of rehabilitating employed people, is designed to train the unemployed either in a cooperating firm or organization, or in conservation maintenance. The rehabilitation hospital approach is more loosely tied to industry or state on the contractual basis (Ambre, 1966). The Job Corps, however, does not have the qualified personnel to handle, to any appreciable extent, the social and psychological deficiencies of many of the candidates. Intellectual assessment may precede training as a screening procedure by someone not attached to the Center, or it may be given after training is begun and impairment is suspected, but the candidate who is found to be grossly defective and "untrainable" is sometimes not given the special attention needed.

The candidates are sometimes placed in large, highly-mechanized workshops where supervision is difficult. The size of these Centers produces an atmosphere of anonymity that is not conducive to an increase in self-identity.

Social adjustment and assimilation into the community are made difficult for the candidate from one region when he is placed in a plant in an entirely different region. In contrast to this policy, the small operating unit that forms a part of the rehabilitation hospital concept is more mobile, and a planned system of relocating the staff and hospital from one part of the country to another might be feasible. A policy of mobility such as this would probably make assimiliation even more difficult, if assimilation is the purpose of the Center personnel. If assimilation could not be accomplished, the small size and "openness" of the rehabilitation hospital model would, nevertheless, afford the possibility of the trainees to find meaningful relationships with one another in geographic regions similar to those of their backgrounds.

The restorative function of the rehabilitation hospital may be lost on some people in the community, although some Job Corps Centers known to the author have made progress along this line. It was demonstrated, however, that the residents in the one community we studied felt that a hospital with such a framework contributed to the economy of the area and of the country. This feeling, in comparison with attitudes toward projects that are seen as "foreign ingredients" to the host community, should not be underestimated in its effect on both the staff and the rehabilitees. The hospital, the firms, and the householders in the area are formed as a cooperative unit for rehabilitating the patients (or enrollees, as the case may be).

Despite efforts to analyze occupational opportunities closely, many people are still trained for non-existing jobs. The rehabilitation hospital plan does not create jobs directly, but simulates their creation within the plan of the organization. The most enduring "creation," however, is the capacity to work inspired in the patients or rehabilitees by their role model staff members.

The Role Model Concept

Implying as it does that one person's behavior and attitudes can be reshaped by "significant others" with whom they are engaging in meaningful activity, the role model concept of rehabilitation can be applied to other areas of social need and current programs with varying degrees of applicability.

An important factor in this success is the ease of flow of communication between staff and trainee. Haigh (1966), for example, illustrates communication problems met by Peace Corps volunteers in their preparatory work with the Pima Indians on the Gila Reservation. Direct questions gave rise to smiling, affirmative replies from the Indians, whereas indirect allusions yielded the important information that the corpsmen sought. The latter type of exchange requires much more language facility and, in a foreign language, the problem is compounded.

The fact that misinformation and misunderstandings in communication may jeopardize any well-conceived rehabilitation program points up the importance of records in assessing the rehabilitee according to the needs of the community and the individual. Several records and checklists were used in the program we described. These were intentionally scaled according to highly observable, overt units of behavior.

It is extremely useful, therefore, to have such an ongoing system both (1) to evaluate the progress or deterioration of work habits accurately, and (2) to maintain contact between the role model and the rehabilitee through the mediation of the work role. Working in another culture, such as the Pima Indians in the example cited, does not diminish this necessity for records, but careful attention should be paid to the culturally derived meaning of these behavioral indices among the people of that culture. Perhaps entirely new sets of items must be found to apply to different groups. These items are best derived from the behavior patterns of those people who are functioning in the particular jobs within that culture setting in a way similar to the way aptitude criteria are gathered.

In programs such as the Peace Corps, the ethical question

of whether role models from one ethnic group and social class should impose their expectations on people of another ethnic group and social class is a real problem and may cause some concern among the staff. Because of the importance that learning a trade in the work role has for the betterment of the host country, this question must be dismissed as long as the members of the society remain poor. Nations, like communities within nations, are interdependent and the prosperity of one influences the continued prosperity of others. In some situations, due care should be exercised to limit the relationship to the work role in another culture, if it is felt that long established and functioning role behavior may be jeopardized in the rehabilitation process.

Given staff members from adult, skilled, semi-skilled and professional, Western, working and middle classes, the following distribution of situations where this plan could be applied is suggested without empirical verification (arranged from the most applicable to the least applicable in terms of the problems of the role models forming a work role relationship with the trainees): (1) Job Corps, except for the age factor, (2) day care centers and centers for homeless men, (3) Peace Corps (in sites for training the trainers), (4) prisons, (5) rehabilitation centers for the physically handicapped, (6) mental hospitals, (7) Neighborhood Youth Corps, (8) reformatories, (9) geriatric hospitals and retirement centers, and (10) Peace Corps (field stations) and other development programs.

Arranging these groups in this way does not place greater value on any one group as opposed to another, nor does it mean that communication and understanding could not be overcome. Arranging the programs in this order suggests that a person wishing to work in rehabilitating geriatric patients, for example, must have some knowledge of the experiencing patient, and that a generation may span the work role relationship. The expectations and stamina of the geriatric patient are markedly different from those of the younger member of the staff. There can still be a renewed personal identity and self-respect built up through work scaled to the capacity of the patient and through the knowledge that he is an important part of a functioning business concern. The problems of working with the geriatric would be greater than the problems of working in a prison, where the age factor would not interfere with the relationship. The reader can reflect on some problems in the other examples mentioned here and would perhaps arrange them differently.

We will discuss a selected number of these other groups, leaving out the mental hospital, the geriatric centers, and Peace Corps field stations, which have already been mentioned. We focus on what modifications might be required and on how the approach could be best applied.

The Job Corps. Mention has been made of how the Job Corps and Neighborhood Youth Corps could use to advantage the ideology and organizational structure of the rehabilitation hospital. The size of the employment problem with regard to the young people these programs are designed to serve and recommendations and weaknesses of these recommendations have been published by the President's Committee on Youth Employment (1963). It is beyond the scope of this book to evaluate the policies and criticisms of this report. The report, however, illuminates the urgency of the problem.

The approach of the rehabilitation hospital is supported by at least one careful analysis of the problem. Kelly and Veldman (1964) studied three groups of male adolescents who were classified as delinquents, school dropouts, and non-deviants still in school. The first two groups differed from the non-deviant group in being generally more impulsive on performance tasks, but their reported needs of dominance were not significantly different. The impulsivity and absence of control of the delinquents and dropouts were present prior to their committing delinquent acts or dropping out of school. The authors of the study raise the possibility that lack of control is a means to gain socially approved dominance among these adolescents. There are present, therefore, personality and social psychological problems that most of the recommendations, including the Committee's report, fail to consider.

Let us recall the point made earlier that the psychological aspects of the poverty victim's problems outweigh many of the remedial efforts publicly discussed; this is also true of the predelinquent, or potential poverty victim, and we need an approach dealing with the impulsivity of adolescents. We do not have direct evidence that the older, mentally ill persons who were studied in the rehabilitation hospital were less impulsive after being there (see Chapter 5), and it is doubtful that impulsivity is a characteristic of the institutionalized person. Nevertheless, a role model approach to the problem of the adolescent is particularly attuned to the adolescent's needs of obtaining dominance. The data on *optimistic* and *intelligent* showing an increase are relevant to this point. Data showing a change in personality dimensions in Chapter 5 and in Appendix B especially underscore this approach as being worthwhile, and these data suggest that a basic means of controlling impulses can be formed in an environment like the rehabilitation hospital.

The Job Corps has taken a step in the direction of making work and education more meaningful for the youth of our country. Quoting statistics and advances due to these programs is encouraging, but to do so dehumanizes the problem when we omit self-image changes. We give vast amounts to such programs to salve the conscience of our generation, and we expect, in return for this investment, to feel secure from riot and crime, the more dramatic outgrowths of the problem. Our own self-image is, therefore, enhanced.

True rehabilitation of the dropout, the predelinquent, and the young person doomed to the street, however, requires something in return from the person it is designed to serve. It is difficult for the young person involved to visualize avoiding delinquency as a contribution to society. A plan whereby the person can see how his productive capacity helps to gain himself and others a vacation and a paycheck yields far more in a shared self-esteem.

In working to construct roles and change social self-image among youths who have been given little societal support in finding jobs, we often find that we must deal with groups with which these youths are affiliated. These groups are formed voluntarily according to age range and interests, and, as "gangs," are characterized by unusual solidarity. Drawing the entire gang formation into such a plan of rehabilitation as we described would have some positive features. Going one step further and creating workshops out of the activities of two rival gangs would certainly be challenging, although the results would be less predictable. There might be certain hazards involved in such a venture that would prevent the occurrence of any real psychological change. The rivalry might be so intense that sublimating it into a program of this sort without greater physical activity, such as games, would be inadvisable. Some method of dealing with or using gang formation is nevertheless necessary where these strong affiliations are present in the social life of the unemployed. The person involved in such relationships has without doubt a more positive prognosis than the person who has an aloof and solitary existence. This lack of relationships in the life of the latter person is more typical of the next group we will consider.

Day Care Centers and Centers for Homeless Men. We include in this category organizations such as special programs for chronic alcoholics and programs sponsored by religious groups. Many of these programs deal principally with the physical comfort of the person, and the people cared for are not institutionalized persons in the sense that we have been discussing elsewhere in this book.[3]

The frequency with which many of these men, who exhibit life-long nomadic behavior, appear for temporary care suggests that a longer and more intensive program might be of some benefit. It also suggests that many would seek to leave the program unannounced and after a short stay. The intervention of the program would mean a sudden change in the "life style" and a lack of social relationships for many. The role model concept would be especially relevant to these cases not only in serving as an anchor for some, but in changing their deviant behavior to more conforming roles and increasing their tolerance for stress.

It is to be anticipated that many of these people would work only until "drinking money" was accumulated; therefore, other measures, such as aversive treatment, might accompany the program.

[3] Their apathy, however, may approximate the "institutional neurosis" described by Barton (1959). We can liken a confining and demoralizing society to an "institution" of a sort. This society tends to encourage social withdrawal and frustration by presenting an underprivileged person with too many "cues" for success. In a similar way, the mental hospital often presents the patient conflicting "cues" for discharge.

Many of these men would soon form the transitory behavior of going from one center to another, as they have already exhibited. Their circuits—from jails, to hospitals, to religious organizations, and such—are frequently predictable. Some type of restriction of this behavior through a centralized bureau would be beneficial, but the "openness" of the scheme should be retained at each center.

The approach would be helpful in training Peace Corps volunteers in at least two ways: (1) the discussion groups woven into the work time would avail the volunteers of an opportunity to evaluate the work as such; (2) tolerance for manual and routine work among some who are unaccustomed to this type of labor would be increased. The same would hold true for the training personnel of Job Corps Training Centers. Role-playing types of situations could be created in the center to simulate the conditions and elucidate the problems to be anticipated in the field. Appropriate rating schemes and checklists could be devised in these centers and the staff could be taught to use them to best advantage by rating one another.

Prisons and Security Hospitals. Security of prisoners and openness of the rehabilitation environment at first glance seem incompatible. Vocational training of a high quality, however, is carried out in many prisons.[4] Many of the prisoners are, unfortunately, thought to be uneducable and are not given an opportunity for this training; in some cases, training is thought to be useless because of the intractable and negative attitude of the prisoner toward society. These men and women (and we include the men and women in hospital/prisons that incarcerate and treat those addicted to drugs) are often labeled "outcasts." As they continue their isolation, the social separation between them and the society widens, and they are very much forgotten persons. The same factors discussed in connection with the need for social re-education of the chronic mental patient exist also for some long-term prisoners.

A plan of rehabilitation can replace physical security with a protective security of confidence. This is based upon the belief that the "outcasts" feel the need to be secure from the ambiguity of their place in a society of overspecialization more than the members of

[4] For a comprehensive review of these programs in a recent publication, see Gibbons (1965).

society feel a need to be secure from them. Antisocial behavior is taken here to be a symptom of a lack of commitment to a goal, in this case, a work role. Antisocial behavior is also a symptom of the impersonalization, or the perception of others as objects rather than as persons, that accompanies specialization. One does not steal from a person perceived as a person, but from a person perceived as an object having some other object one wants to possess; to some extent, this principle is vividly displayed in riot behavior. When the criminal finds that he is a "wanted man," he begins to perceive himself as an object and not as a true person. This dilemma in our society has been most elegantly presented by Erich Fromm (1947) as man's indifference to himself. Fromm calls this indifference man's greatest moral problem.

It has been mentioned that occupation is thought to fulfill a variety of basic human needs. Overspecialization within occupational roles fulfills the same needs (such as the "need for esteem"), but tends to stultify the person with a rigidity of performance that depersonalizes the worker. Depersonalization is, admittedly, only one effect. It is a basis, however, for many other social problems discussed here—for example, the plight of the "homeless men" in our society, for whom this tendency toward depersonalization is augmented by our treatment of them.

In contrast to many prison programs, the approach of the rehabilitation hospital is conducted primarily in an ideological environment where personal worth and competence are valued. The fact that the attitudes of those who surround the person in his work are a determining factor in mental breakdown has been analyzed by Simmons (1964). In a similar manner, attitudes of peers and work associates often determine whether a man returns to prison or remains on the job. This rehabilitation plan can form for the prisoner a valuable, personalizing experience, wherein he can earn money in a business concern in which he has invested time and energy, as well as a part of his earnings.

A prepared environment such as the one described here may become a permanent placement for some, but for many it can serve as a "bridge" to society. We believe that the rehabilitation/hospital's lack of physical security makes for an environment that is less tempting a haven for the ex-prisoner to return to than an environment that shelters him from society.

Rehabilitation Centers for the Physically Handicapped. The next few paragraphs deal with hospitals and training schools for the mental defective and epileptic. A great deal of inspired work has been done in the assessment of the physically disabled. One program that matches the results of a large variety of situation tasks and subsequent retraining is the TOWER system (Testing, Orientation and Work Evaluation in Rehabilitation, 1959). Similar evaluations are conducted in the rehabilitation hospital.

An important point to reiterate here is the fact that confirmed organic deficit was found not to contraindicate a good adjustment to the program. The number of seizure-prone epileptics without particular psychotic or neurotic reactions who have been successfully employed suggests that even those persons with psychotic or neurotic reactions can be managed in a suitable environment.

The chief differences of this plan from existing programs are its social re-education program and use of the hospital as a business enterprise. For many physically handicapped people, the social re-education program would be unnecessary, except to train them to operate common devices, such as drills, while using prosthetic aids. Group discussions pertaining to their feelings toward their disability and their responsibilities after discharge, and informing them of possible employment, could be added to any program with advantage. A more exacting observation of their compensatory psychological mechanisms and physiological movements than is given the other groups considered is necessary for the physically handicapped.

Many features of the rehabilitation hospital, such as the newsletter giving an account of the output for the week, would be helpful in assimilating these people, who are often highly conscious of their output into the rehabilitation center community. Concealing such information often arouses fantasies of being unworthy of the treatment being given them.

Once again the personal care taken of each person's needs and the flexibility of the plan in meeting these needs make the rehabilitation hospital idea uniquely suited to the physically as well as the mentally handicapped. Attention should be paid to a progression of responsibilities so as to present to the physically disabled some goal toward which he may strive. The environment should not cater to his disability, but should be geared in such a way that he should have no fear of injury. Simply taking away a cane when it is felt that it is of no further use to the disabled person and substituting for it careful encouragement by all members of the staff is sometimes all that needs to be done. This was done in one instance in the rehabilitation hospital studied, and the patient in question was soon able to walk without the aid of other patients to and from his workshop.

◆§ *SUMMARY* §◆

From the work that we have reviewed in the rehabilitation hospital, considering the severity of the psychopathology of the patients being rehabilitated there, we find hope that through such a plan the culturally deprived and the "outcasts," who are being amassed by the type of society that we have created, can also be reclaimed.

The approach brings together in cross-fertilization two areas of present-day national concern: poverty and mental illness. As Americans, we tend to look to the future with "brick-and-mortar," "dollar-and-cents" solutions. In the area of mental illness, as in antipoverty programs, our answers to the problems have been typical. The primary need seems to be to find some way of identifying the mentally sick person in the community and to treat him there. Proposals of this kind have been published by the Joint Committee on Mental Illness and Health in 1961; they encourage the use of community facilities for the prevention of mental illness. In contrast, the rehabilitation approach investigated in this book emphasizes returning to society a great number of those disturbed people who were unfortunate enough to be hospitalized before community mental health became a matter of policy and debate.

In years past, when the society was more simple and less "computerized," this return did not pose the hazards that it does today. Special preparation is now necessary and, we believe, requires an environment that gradually refocuses the patients' attention toward the areas of interpersonal relationships and extension of responsibilities.

By expressing this method of rehabilitation through the hospital *cum* factory in terms of the work role, it enables us to broaden its application considerably. The implication is that work, as a goal-directed activity important as a value in our society and therefore to the social self-image, can be harnessed in constructing a trusting relationship between people. These relationships are eroding with increasing demands for specialization where people are bought and sold as commodities, or as repositories of needed skills.

The most promising extension of the program is in the rehabilitation of the jobless and particularly of those who are thought to be unapproachable by other means.

There are many roads to the ranks of the unemployable beyond being displaced by automation or, like an adolescent of my acquaintance, having the attitude that work is "just for fools." Many factors are involved in a complex society, and its very complexity emerges, in many current analyses, as a cause of the problem.

This complexity is often stated in terms of work specialization that creates the appealing variety of consumer products of our society. Specialization is not entirely damaging; on the contrary, the comfort and health of the members of societies would be very poor without it. Overspecialization has the effect, however, of separating those who are emotionally able to specialize and those who require a broader view; thus overspecialization results in unhappy people, and it sometimes exacerbates the symptoms of mentally unhealthy persons. It results in certain poorly-endowed people being unable to intellectually understand the greater demand for detail (and abstractions), which comes through fragmenting vocations into specialties, in their chosen line of work. Some of these people may view their future vocation in a highly idealized perspective, which they have gained through popular media, and become disillusioned with the fact that what they must learn involves what appears to be drab rote memory. It results in seemingly endless qualifications and, for some, compounding degrees until the productive years are past and no real work role has been experienced.

The approach of the hospital/factory does not necessarily introduce another specialty into the field of mental health, that is, the specialty of being a role model. Rather, such a model-patient relationship is the basis for many group and individual therapies, particularly those of the more active, short-term, and counseling variety. There is evidence, moreover, that, due to the numbers of underprivileged, disturbed people to be treated, and the results of research that is being conducted, the needs of the society can best be served by the active intervention of the therapists. An active intervention of a total milieu is required in many instances. Applying this technique of rehabilitation with an emphasis on the total milieu to, for example, the school dropout or delinquent, gives us an opportunity to replace beneficial role models for detrimental ones.

Through a series of investigations into the therapeutic function of the hospital chosen for analysis, we found a relationship between the various attitudes of the staff, some of whom served as role models, and the structure of the hospital. Some aspects of custodialism, for example, were emphasized and considered necessary for rehabilitation. Achievement through such a program was found to be associated with some characteristics of the patients and not with others; these characteristics are probably important in the rehabilitation of the poor in such a plan.

We have discussed such diverse topics as the theoretical factors underlying a change in self-image or the institutionalized person, the requirements as to types of work that fit the program, and the need for social re-education. The scope of our analysis has, therefore, been both theoretical and intensely practical to the needs of many in this country and at this time. We have been bold enough to envision the addition of a new and corrective environment to the matrix of our society in an effort to counteract the depersonalizing effects of the old. Perhaps through making an effort for the benefit of our needy in this way we can add a little more luster to our collective self-image among the nations of the world.

Description:
Study I

We designated a probability of .05 as our level of significance in rejecting or supporting our assumptions. We used one-tailed tests; when further analyses were suggested by the data, we used two-tailed tests.

Tests applied to the results in these appendices were either chi square or exact probability calculations. The rules by which we chose these methods are to be found in Walker and Lev (1953, p. 107). Whenever there was an expected frequency of less than 5, we applied the Fisher Test of exact probabilities, except for the 2 or more degrees of freedom. In these cases, an expectation of only 2 in a cell was sufficient for the chi square approximations (Walker and Lev, 1953).

✌§ SUBJECTS §❧

The records of ninety-two patients, serving as the sources of our data, were kept in the units. There were thirty-eight male patients in Blue, twenty-nine in Gold; there were fourteen female patients in Blue and eleven in Gold. All patients had been in the rehabilitation hospital at least a year. All Gold patients had been advanced through the units. Some had gone directly from Grey to Gold Unit without traversing the intermediate steps. Two had returned from outside employment while in this unit. None of the Blue patients had been in Gold, but some had been in Red Unit, the next stage toward Gold, and these had been returned to Blue Unit after unsuccessful attempts there.

The mean number of months that the patients had been in the rehabilitation hospital was not significantly different: Blue Unit, 28.1; Gold Unit, 26.0. Fifty-five, or 60 per cent, of the patients had been admitted during the first seven months of operation of the hospital. Of these fifty-five, thirty, or 54.5 per cent, were in Blue Unit, and twenty-five, or 45.5 per cent, were in Gold Unit. There was a tendency for the non-achievers to have been in the hospital for a longer period, but the group was essentially comparable in this regard. The time spent in the rehabilitation hospital for this sample was skewed toward the earlier months of the two years represented.

The patients were diagnosed either as schizophrenic or as "others" (paraphrenia, depression, anxiety neurosis, paresis, manic depressive psychosis, paranoid state, and involutional psychosis). There were significantly more schizophrenic patients in Blue Unit. The patients in both units were predominantly schizophrenic, as was to be expected, but this was most markedly so among the non-achievers (see Table A-1).

The difference in intelligence of the patients was not found because the length of time of some patients more than others in the program would bias the results. It is conceivable that the Gold Unit patients might perform better on the tests because they had experienced all of the steps in the program. Intelligence of the patients is reported in another connection in Appendix G.

MEASURES AND METHODOLOGY

Hollingshead's 2-factor index was used in determining the social class of the patients (Hollingshead, 1957). The rural-urban designation was found in the list of primary occupations in the case-papers. The time spent in the parent hospitals, weekly earnings, age at admission to the rehabilitation hospital, days in the clinic, and incidence of psychosurgery were obtained from the same source.

The work reports are filled out for each review committee meeting and, as indicated in Chapter Three, one patient may have several reports in his file. The patient's performance in the workshop or on an outside assignment, such as gardening, for a given period of time is rated along a five-point scale on twelve factors. The ratings are weighted according to the following categories: weight of zero when "A applies"; weight of one when "inclined to A"; weight of two when "about average"; weight of three when "inclined to B"; weight of four when "B applies." The range of scores, therefore, is from zero, or all A's, to 48, or all B's. The behavior items are:

1. The patient carries out complicated, or only simple tasks.
2. He will look for work when task is complete, or he must be given work to do.

3. He will work for long, or only for short periods.
4. He grasps instructions quickly, or cannot do so at all.
5. He always finishes his job, or never completes one.
6. He gets on by himself, or needs continual prompting.
7. He is eager to work, or avoids it.
8. He communicates, or does not communicate, with staff members.
9. He communicates, or does not communicate, with patients spontaneously.
10. He works at a good speed, or is slow.
11. He wastes and destroys, or does not waste and destroy, materials.
12. He is never late for work, or is always late for work.

The total scores were computed, and these served as the measures used in the analysis.

The work report scores and the earnings for the first assessment periods, or the first six months, were analyzed because, during this time, the patients were on more uniform tasks in terms of wages. They were usually in Grey or Red Units.

This time period was also taken as representative in order to account for normal fluctuations and holiday pay. The wages earned during the first three-week assessment period would be an unrealistic measure of achievement because the flat rates paid for the time spent in the various sections of the hospital are given the patients then. These wages would not be indicative of any real initiative.

It is important to understand here that the wages were untaxed income and were over and above the costs of caring for the patient. The figures that are given as the patients' earnings during this six-month period when the research was conducted can be converted into dollars at $2.80 equaling one pound sterling. The patients' weekly wages ordinarily vary widely. The greater difference between the rates of payment for the jobs done do not occur until later when the patients are in the more "advanced" Gold Unit or the less "advanced" Blue Unit. The disparity between high-paying and lower-paying jobs was a difficulty in this sort of analysis. At the time in the history of the hospital when these data were recorded, only two units were in operation, and the jobs were repetitive and standardized in terms of payment. The disparity was not as great between jobs as at the present time. For this reason, these data are those earnings made by the Gold and Blue Unit patients when they were working in Grey and Red Units at the outset of the program.

Unfortunately, there were no data available for an estimate of reliability and validity of the work report. In an effort to establish validity, we related two measures, the scores and earnings, on the same subjects. The work report scores were normally distributed; the earnings were not. The associations between these data for the same period of time were: $r_s = .287$, $t = 1.78$, $df = 38$, $p < .05$ for Gold Unit, and $r_s = .65$, $t = 6.03$, $df = 50$, $p < .001$ for Blue Unit.

Job changes were measured by the number of different tasks noted on the work reports for the same period of time for all patients. The patients had all been in the hospital for at least one year, and it was during the first year that the number of jobs was found for each patient. There had been no major policy change of job allocation during this time so that no bias was obvious in these comparisons.

Special mention should be made of the factor of family expectations. We surveyed the correspondence between the hospital and the family and consulted the social workers for these data.

Data on the family were divided for analysis between siblings and parents or wife.[1] Only those responses that were proven to be unequivocal were used. There was no difference between the units in the interest of the family members in the patients (see Table A-1).

ᴥৡ RESULTS AND DISCUSSION ৡᴥ

A summary of the results appears in Table A-1. Frequent references will be made to this table in the pages to follow.

---

[1] The categories of parents and wife were combined because many patients were unmarried, or widowed; many others had parents deceased or unknown. In some cases, the patients were not living with family members prior to hospitalization, but reactions were routinely gathered from these family members.

TABLE A-1

Summary of Results of Analyses of Factors
Among Achievers and Non-Achievers

FACTORS	χ^2	P
Diagnoses	13.60	<.001
Willingness of Family		
Siblings	.0003*	
Parents/Wives	.2917*	N.S.
Urban/rural	.059	N.S.
Psychosurgery	2.56	<.20 N.S.
Clinic Residence	4.25	<.05
Marital Status (Total)	3.77	<.10 N.S.
Marital Status (Schizophrenics)	2.30	<.20 N.S.
Marital Status (Male)	8.396	<.01
Marital status (Female)	.0414*	
Sex (Schizophrenics)	3.245	<.10 N.S.
Work Score Change (Total)	3.257	<.10 N.S.
Work Score Change (Male)	5.53	<.02
Wages (Total)	8.67**	<.01
Wages (Male)	.812**	N.S.

* Fisher Exact Probability Test
** Median Test

The social class data were as follows: Class II (highest), Gold, three patients, Blue, one; Class III, Gold, sixteen, Blue, twenty; Class IV, Gold, fourteen, Blue, sixteen; Class V, Gold, six, Blue, seven. There was one patient in Gold and seven in Blue for whom social class was unknown by reason of inadequate information. Dichotomizing Classes II–III and IV–V for the eighty-four cases, we find no significance between the social classes.

In testing the second prediction concerning rural-urban differences, we should note a difference between nations. In previous research, dealing with prognostic differences, extremes regarding rural and urban settings were first isolated (Query and Query, 1964). The incidence of discharge of patients from these disparate backgrounds was investigated. Not only were the urban and rural patients in the rehabilitation hospital less sharply distinguished for the purposes of this study, but the rural patient in the region of England where the rehabilitation hospital is located is not to be equated with the Kentucky mountain patient studied in the previous research. There is no assurance also that the rural patients here were not reared in cities, nor, for that matter, that the urban patients were not reared in rural settings, as many of them might have been during the extreme circumstances of the war. The data deal only with the principal premorbid occupations known to have been held by the subjects.

There is no difference between the achievers and non-achievers concerning this variable (see Table A-1). ·

The tests were computed between the means of the years spent in the parent hospitals and age at the time of admission to the rehabilitation hospital, as shown by the case-papers for the respective groups. The results are reported in Table A-2.

TABLE A-2

Differences Between Years in Parent Hospital and
Age at Admission to Rehabilitation

		Units		
Gold (N = 40)		Blue (N = 52)		t/p
Years in	Mean	12.7	14.7	1.35 < .10
"Parent"	SD	7.315	6.440	
Hospital				
Age at	Mean	46.0	40.4	4.83 < .001
Admission	SD	7.570	3.480	

We predicted that Gold Unit patients, or achievers, would show fewer years of hospitalization and be younger at admission. The first of these predictions is not borne out, and there is a significant reversal of the second prediction.

It is interesting to note the age at which rehabilitation started in view of the age ceiling for admission mentioned in Chapter 3. This upper age limit was fifty-five, only nine years older than the mean age for the Gold Unit patients.

Perhaps because the achievers are less a threat, siblings are less willing to take the non-achiever than the achiever, whereas this makes little difference to the parents and/or wives, as seen in Table A-1.

Lobotomization of patients was suggested to be a factor interfering with the rehabilitation process. Special retraining of most patients with organic deficit is usually required. Although there is a trend suggesting that more non-achievers than achievers had this type of treatment, the results are not significant, as Table A-1 reveals.

We also suggested that fewer days in the clinic would characterize the achiever. Only one patient in Gold Unit showed any time at all spent for psychiatric reasons in the clinic. Eight non-achieving patients spent time in the clinic. Fourteen clinic days were represented by the single achiever, and a mean of 18.5 days, or a total of 148 days, for the eight non-achievers. There was a significant difference found along this dimension (Table A-1).

Although still an open question, some researchers have suggested that marital status is positively related to "good" prognosis. For purposes of consistency we will first test this factor among all patients, regardless of diagnosis. The analysis in Table A-1 failed to confirm this suggestion, however, although a trend is clear.

Data of the schizophrenic patients were next considered alone.

These analyses show only a trend toward a relationship in the one case, or .10 level of confidence, and none in the other. Another way of looking at these findings is that all the married non-achievers are schizophrenic, whereas only 64 per cent of the married achievers are schizophrenic. The conclusion is that marriage is not a significant factor in terms of rehabilitation potential, nor is it related to diagnosis.

An additional factor, sex of the patient, must be taken into account when comparing these data with former investigations of prognosis. Previous investigators have used only male patients for their conclusions in pointing out the importance of marriage. When male patients are considered alone, the findings are significant, as shown in Table A-1.

We must amend our findings to indicate that marriage is most significant when male patients are considered.

The same data for female patients were analyzed and a reversal was found, with more married non-achievers and the same number of single patients in both groups.

The sex of the patient emerges as crucial in explaining the impact that marital status has upon rehabilitation prospects as defined here. Is schizophrenia more important for non-achievement among single females than among single males? Among achievers, one female and eight males were schizophrenic; among non-achievers, four females and five males were schizophrenic ($p < .001$, Fisher Test). The achievers tended to be male among the schizophrenics, and the answer is "yes." Irrespective of marital status, there is a tendency (not significant) for schizophrenia to be more important for non-achievement among females. The next test reported in Table A-1 is for schizophrenics by sex according to achievement and indicates that female schizophrenics achieve much less than males.

Other predictions were that the achievers would have "better," or lower, work report scores than non-achievers at the beginning of rehabilitation, and there would be no decrease during the period. They would have more job changes, and they would have higher earnings.

The mean and standard deviations of the work scores for Gold and Blue were: mean = 16.85, SD = 7.86; mean = 30.87, SD = 8.05 ($t = 8.39$, $p < .001$) respectively, for the first assessment. For the last assessment, the Gold and Blue means and standard deviations were, respectively: mean = 16.30, SD = 8.03; mean = 24.65, SD = 8.13 ($t = 4.82$, $p < .001$).

The achievers had significantly lower scores for both assessments. The change of the individual scores between the periods for the two groups was analyzed by chi square.[2] The few "same" reports were placed with the decrease scores for purposes of analysis, and the scores were dichotomized as "better," "worse," or "no change." The data appear in Table A-1.

---

[2] Obviously some reports were separated by slightly more months elapsing between the first and last assessments than others, because some patients had been in the hospital for a longer period of time. One will recall that there was no difference between units on this variable (length of time in the hospital), so that the report changes were comparable.

Although the achievers have better scores, the analysis of change showed a slight trend toward reversal of the prediction in favor of the non-achievers. These findings are even more apparent when the data for the men alone are analyzed, as they are reported in the same table. This relationship was unique to the male patient (for female patients, $p = .303$, Fisher test).

We conclude that the achievers, particularly the men, are given such a "good" report at the outset that little latitude is left for further rated improvement. The non-achievers are still significantly differentiated from the achievers, despite their overall tendency toward improvement. This interpretation does not explain the low level, denoting extremely poor performance, of some Gold Unit scores. These data, therefore, certainly reflect that greater emphasis is placed in Blue Unit than in the comparison unit on working with the male patients on further improvement. The two unit staffs may also be using a different standard of excellence, and this is, in part, the topic of another part of the hospital evaluation.

The results of the analysis of number of different jobs given the patients in the two groups were significant ($t = 5.63$, $p < .001$). The means and standard deviations were Gold Unit, mean $= 12.23$, SD $= 3.565$; Blue Unit, mean $= 8.33$, SD $= 3.08$.

The prediction that the achievers would have a greater variety of tasks given them is substantiated and highlights the importance of flexibility in rehabilitation. It is important to realize that these data represent jobs for the entire two-year period, and that they do not suggest different initial experiences of the patients in the units. The large number of different jobs, or relatively few jobs, as the case may be, is only partly a function of the nature of the units. It was mentioned in Chapter 3 that the patients in Blue Unit have more standard jobs than the patients in the other units. At the same time, during the first months of operation, the patients in both units were given routine and unchanging tasks so that the variety of changes in the achieving patients' experience occurred relatively late in the two-year period.

On the basis of past performance in the parent hospital, it was expected that the achievers would show greater rehabilitation potential early by earning higher wages than the non-achievers during the first half-year of hospitalization. Table A-1 contains the data and a critical test between the groups. The respective means were found to be £20/12/6 for the achievers and £16/2/0 for the non-achievers. The data were found also to be markedly skewed toward the lesser wages, so that a nonparametric measure was used for the test of significance (the median test). The median was found to be £16/18/5 (six months).

The results reported in Table A-1 are in agreement with the findings pertaining to the positive relationship between work report scores and wages, that is, that scores were significantly lower for achievers than non-achievers.

The finding that married men have a better prognosis generally suggests that their earning power would be greater than unmarried men for reasons both of being able to form an intimate relationship in marriage and of the financial responsibility marriage entails even while in the hospital. The data for the married versus single men were grouped for analysis, regardless of which unit the patients occupied. We will first analyze the married patients' initial and recent work report scores.

For the married and single men respectively, the data were: mean = 19.8, SD = 11.04; mean = 26.5, SD = 9.84 (t = 3.38, p < .001) for the first assessment. For the last assessment, mean = 17.3, SD = 8.53; mean = 21.9, SD = 8.45 (t = 2.80, p < .01).

We find that the patients in both marital status groups have "better" scores as expected, and there are significant differences between the groups throughout the two assessment periods. The next analysis was done for these sixty-seven male patients in the same way as between the units, that is, by finding the median wage. The median was £18/3/5½. The analysis is shown in Table A-1.

Despite the correspondence between wages earned and work score rating, married men do not tend to earn more than single men regardless of achievement status. There is a slight trend in the predicted direction, which fails to be significant. This result may be related to the lack of difference in family attitudes previously found, inasmuch as there might be no greater anticipated return of the married men to their families over the single men, and so no incentive on this basis to earn to support their families.

We related marital status among the men according to family attitudes of dependents (wives and parents), in order to gain some understanding of the relationship. The fact that the single men had no wife to be interested in them is not as contaminating as it appears. The reason for this is that only 27 per cent of the men were married. It will be recalled that some parents were deceased, so that only fifty-one cases were used in this analysis. We felt justified in retaining all cases for analysis where either a parent or a wife was found to be living. The analysis is shown in the last row of Table A-1.

No significant difference between marital status and family attitude is shown. Indeed, a greater number of married men have less incentive to earn, because their families show less interest (either wife or parent) in them than do the families of single men. Whether this interest would be increased as the married men earned more with continued stay in the hospital is a legitimate point of conjecture.

Description: Study II

↝§ SUBJECTS §↜

Initial screening of patients for subjects in this experiment was done with the Wechsler Adult Intelligence Scale. We used patients who could read and understand the meaning of the self-image traits. A score of at least eight standard score points on the Vocabulary subtest was necessary. Out of a pool of 104 patients who met this criterion, seventy-two—in three groups of twenty-four (fourteen men and ten women)—were found to be comparable in age and years of hospitalization. The groups were significantly different only in the months the members had spent in the rehabilitation hospital. The mean for the short-stay group was 4.3 months; the mean for the medium-stay group was 14.1 months; and the mean for the long-stay group was 26.0 months, and these patients were considered good or fair candidates for rehabilitation; many were actually working as day patients; some were discharged and others had been returned after a period of employment. These patients were included as subjects in the long-stay group in order to have the number required for analysis.

The criterion of adequate intelligence was important for another reason. The test we chose was a self-report, objective inventory to test personality adjustment. Adequate reading ability was required to take the test.

↝§ MEASURES AND METHODOLOGY §↜

The test most amenable as a measure of this concept of personality is the California Psychological Inventory (CPI)[1] (Gough,

[1] The CPI scales are: 1. Dominance, 2. Capacity for status, 3. Sociability, 4. Social presence, 5. Self-acceptance, 6. Sense of well-being, 7. Responsibility, 8. Socialization, 9. Self-control, 10. Tolerance, 11. Good impression, 12. Communality, 13. Achievement via conformance, 14. Achievement via independence, 15. Intellectual efficiency, 16. Psychological-mindedness, 17. Flexibility, and 18. Femininity. In analyzing the results of this test, we made particular note of the Good impression, Communality and Sense of well-being scales in order to ascertain "faking" on the part of the patients, and indiscriminate use of the scale items. In some cases, there have been instances of this, but none appeared in these data. The reliability data among institutionalized per-

1960). It required an average reading ability, and the subjects were selected with this requirement in mind.

Patients of less intelligence also are frequently unable to take cognizance of a continuum. The traits (Appendix C) were placed on a five-point scale from "This does not describe me at all," "About average," to "This describes me to a strong degree," and the patients in the various groups were asked to check where they would place themselves on this continuum. Close attention was paid to their markings as some patients tend to exhibit position effects and stereotyped marking. A sample of the scale was given to them to study before the ratings were performed. The positive and negative traits were alternated on the forms. The role model staff members were all nurses; they rated the patients on the same traits, with appropriate changes in the instructions.

Combined reliability of the measure was found to be .87 (p < .01) for patients and staff members when ten patients not in the experiment and two non-members of the staff (wives of the staff) made ratings six weeks apart.

The CPI was administered to the patients in the short-stay group at the beginning of the assessment and again, as a retest along with the trait questionnaire, after nine months. Three patients of the twenty-four in this group were lost by attrition through discharges, and the CPI data are reported for twenty-one patients (thirteen men and eight women).

We cannot generalize to the entire patient population because of the small number of patients, and because only those intellectually capable of performing the tests were selected. We cannot present firm conclusions for subnormal patients, of whom there are some in the rehabilitation hospital. The patients seen in this study, however, were of low average intelligence and of a variety of diagnoses, and therefore represent the majority of patients in the hospital. They also more nearly represent non-psychotic and non-institutionalized persons outside the hospital, and in their low average intelligence they approximate the unemployed group to which we gener-

---

sons (male inmates) range from .49 (Flexibility) to .87 (Tolerance), so that we were reasonably confident of the reliability of the differences that we might find.

alized our findings in Chapter 8. This is an important fact to consider in discussing the general applicability of the hospital to rehabilitation of people other than mental patients.

The variables of social expectations and reference group affiliation were tested by a card-sorting technique modified for this purpose.

Thirty-two patients were randomly selected from the short-stay and long-stay groups. It was not possible in the time allowed for this research in taking the patients from their jobs to use all of the short- and long-stay patients. There were eight short-stay and long-stay men and the same number of women in each group. Each patient sorted fifty cards four times. The sorting box held three sections in which the cards were placed. The sections were designated "Yes," "No," and "Don't know." The subjects were given instructions to limit the number of "Don't know" cards as much as possible. The phrases printed on the cards (see Appendix D) were constructed to form a meaningful end of a complete sentence, and the stems of the sentences were placed on movable tabs at the top of the sorting box. The tabs were changed by the examiner in the presence of the subject. They were changed in the following sequence:

1. "I am able to ———" (present expectation)
2. "I will be able to ———" (future expectation)
3. "The staff at St. Wulstan's expect me to ———" (rehabilitation hospital reference group)
4. "Most mental patients are able to ———" (patient reference group)

The cards were sorted for each subject between trials, and the subjects placed the cards into the box according to the categories. There was no time limit. The fourth trial sentence stem was further explained to the subject to mean the typical mental patient in the parent hospital. Care was taken to explain that the future expectation, or third sorting, was to be done as though the patient were living outside of the rehabilitation hospital.

The cards were divided into sixteen items pertaining to domestic types of behavior and duties, such as cooking a meal for oneself, sixteen pertaining to the person's emotional life, such as "not getting angry," and nineteen pertaining to occupational aspirations.

Seven of the latter were slanted more toward the rehabilitation hospital workshop or working parties. Twelve involved employment outside the hospital. These latter twelve were subdivided into six realistic and six grossly unrealistic expectations, such as expecting to be elected a member of Parliament. A problem arose in selecting items sensible to both male and female patients, particularly concerning expectations of personal hygiene and types of employment. Rather than arranging two sortings with a further subdivision and thereby extending the time to take the test, the sentences were worded as broadly as possible to take into consideration both men and women. An example would be: "I am able to —— shave, wash, and/or be clean each morning."

The scope of these sortings enabled us to assess several assumptions based upon environmental change.

Other predictions of this study are a series of five expected findings, and are concerned with the differential expectations between the two groups: (A.) The long-stay patients will show a greater number of realistic occupational present and future goals than the short-stay patients. The short-stay patients will show greater unrealistic expectations. (B.) The short-stay group will show collectively greater future expectations than the long-stay group, because of their greater independence of the role model. (C.) Because of the uncertainty of the work role among the short-stay patients, the number of "don't knows" in both patient and rehabilitation hospital reference group sortings will be greater in this group than in the other group. it is true that we anticipate that independence will be fostered after an interim of dependency on the role model, and that the long-stay group will show some independence. We believe that the effects of dependency will still be strong and that a difference will be found owing to the period of dependency in the rehabilitation hospital environment. Easing dependency is one of the problems of rehabilitation and is common to all psychiatric facilities that house the long-term patient. Being uncertain in one's work role is not inconsistent with independence among the short-stay patients because the independence of future expectations is built up in the preselection of the patient before his admission. The patient comes to the rehabilitation hospital seeing himself as being selected for independent work at some undetermined time.[2] He is unsure of what the rehabilitation hospital holds for him, but at the other end awaits a job. He has little insight into the role of the staff in achieving this end. (D.) The short-stay group of patients will show greater mental patient reference group affiliation than the long-stay group. This will be revealed in a greater congruence in the sortings between present expectations ("I am able to ———") and ("Most mental patients are able to ———"). (E.) The long-stay group will have greater congruence between present expectations and the rehabilitation hospital reference group sortings ("The staff of St. Wulstan's expect me to be able to ———") than the short-stay group. The affiliation of the long-stay patients will be shown in this way.

⋙ RESULTS AND DISCUSSION ⋘

The personality of the patient is of fundamental importance, and the data analysis pertaining to this factor is reported first so that the results can be woven into the discussion of the self-image perceptions.

The thesis that personality, as a relatively stable series of clinically testable psychological traits, remains unchanged in the rehabilitation hospital was not substantiated by retesting the short-stay patients. The data for this analysis are reported separately for men and women because of the differences obscured by the tests of change on the combined data. We found the differences for each patient in standard scores. In Table B-1 no sign indicates a rise in this psychological scale; a minus indicates a reduction in the scale score.

Over half of the scales (twelve out of eighteen) show a decrease upon retesting, signifying a generally poorer level of adjustment. In some cases, the direction of the change on the scales parallels a change in self-image. An example of this is the increase in

---

[2] In this connection it is usually found that the patient anticipates that he will remain in the rehabilitation hospital for a far shorter time than the staff believes that he will remain there in view of his condition. This is more noticeable among younger patients and those who have a longer history of working outside the hospital.

TABLE B-1

Mean Change in Patients' CPI Standard Scores

Scales	Men	Women	t^a
Dominance	.8	0	3.778***
Capacity for status	−.4	1	4.640***
Sociability	0	3	3.775***
Social presence	1	.3	3.210***
Self-acceptance	.4	−2	4.867***
Sense of well-being	−2.8	1	2.278*
Responsibility	−.4	.7	3.026***
Socialization	−2.4	2.3	3.310***
Self-control	−3	−1	2.334*
Tolerance	−2	1	3.420***
Good impression	−2	.7	3.456***
Communality	.2	−1	3.000***
Achievement v. conf.	−2.4	2.3	3.405***
Achievement v. ind.	−.4	.3	4.960***
Intellectual efficiency	−1.4	1	6.626***
Psychological-mindedness	.8	.3	2.910***
Flexibility	−2	−.7	2.145*
Femininity	1.8	1	2.528**

^{a} t test of differences between test-retest for all Ss
 * p < .05, 20 df
 ** p < .02
 *** p < .01

femininity among the men with an accompanying lack of predicted shift toward a more masculine self-image. The men generally showed a greater decrease in scale scores in contrast to the women. None of the mean changes were greater than one standard deviation of the scores, but all were significant changes. The greatest overall change for men was noted in *socialization, sense of well-being,* and *achievement via conformance.* These scales are of special importance to a hospital program designed to achieve rehabilitation through work conformity and social pressure. The data from the women, however, showed a marked increase in two of these areas: *socialization* and *achievement via conformance,* and, also, *sociability. Self-acceptance* was reduced among the female patients as a generalized trait. Despite the results pertaining to *intelligence* as a self-image that increases in the hospital, *intellectual efficiency* was one of the scales showing the greatest change, and this trait diminishes among the men.

Underlying this research was the conviction that treatment in a rehabilitation hospital serves to alter the perception of the self-image (along, as we have found, with some aspects of the psychological dimensions of personality). All facets of living in the rehabilitation hospital were grossly dissimilar from anything that the institutionalized person had known before, and we believed that change would involve not only that person's image of himself but also the causes of his illness.

The literature contains at least one reported study where the patient's perception of his illness was shown to be determined by the treatment he is given, and the relevant finding for our consideration is that members of the chronic group (with a reported mean hospitalization of 9.4 years) failed to view any functional reasons for their own hospitalization and the hospitalization of others on their ward even after experience in psychotherapy (Whitman and Duffey, 1961). We did not measure the image our patients had of others. This research, however, gave us cause to reconsider our term *sick* as used in the ratings. The tenacity with which patients cling to physical reasons for being hospitalized suggests that our subjects were not interpreting the *sick* self-image in functional, or psychologic, terms. We were aware of this possibility before retesting our short-stay group a second time. We specified the term *mentally sick* on the repeated forms in order to ascertain any change in meaning. In all other aspects the forms were identical.

Four of the twenty-four members of the short-stay group were returned to the parent hospitals and not seen a second time. The twenty remaining were readministered the self-image test. We anticipated an approximation at best of the medium-stay data, as this latter group had been in the hospital for over a year. The short-stay patients were retested seven to eight months after their first interview. Congruence with the same role models' image of them was again calculated. The same role models were used for these data, although seven of the short-stay patients had moved to other units and were working with other staff members. The role models remained constant for these patients.

In the first series of tests the extremes of the continua were used. Only one prediction was significant because only a small number of patients rated the extremes. The adjective trait, *likable,* was significant (p < .05). There were several trends detectable so that the negative and positive categories were combined and the forty self-image traits were analyzed in dichotomous categories for the three groups, short-stay, medium-stay, and long-stay.

Each trait is discussed before proceding with the data from the staff members and their relationship with the patients' ratings of themselves.

TABLE B-2

Self-image Changes Among Three Groups of Patients

Self-image Trait	χ^2	p	Number of "Average"*
Active	.05	N.S.	35
Anxious	3.18	N.S.	26
Confident	6.38	<.05	25
Dependent	4.27	<.20 N.S.	29
Independent	2.14	N.S.	26
Easily hurt	5.78	<.10 N.S.	24
Hard-working	2.16	N.S.	37
Likable	9.25	<.01	31
Optimistic	6.41	<.05	29
Sick	.06	N.S.	26
Slow	3.71	<.20 N.S.	32
Valuable	1.86	N.S.	30
Absent-minded	11.47	<.01	29
Intelligent	5.93	<.10 N.S.	37
Grave	6.65	<.05	37
Strong	9.82	<.01	34
Neat	5.68	<.10 N.S.	31
Moody	2.69	N.S.	27

* Denotes the number of patients (N = 72) who rated themselves as "average" on the trait.

The prediction that an increase in "yes" responses with time on activity and change in anxiousness was not confirmed. Almost half of the patients rated themselves "average" on these traits as they did on most of them (Table B-2).

These data were not significant, but were found to be aligned in the predicted direction. Twice as many patients in the short-stay group noted "no" to being *anxious*, and a reversal was found in the middle-stay group. This result was expected as pressure for greater achievement grows. The last group showed a tendency to return to the distribution revealed among the short-stay patients. This result may have been a chance factor.

Confidence data were significant as shown in the table.

Approximately half of the patients newly admitted, or seen within a few months of their admission, asserted by way of their responses to the questionnaire that they were not confident. One might expect that confidence would characterize a patient who had been chosen for admission to the rehabilitation hospital. This did not seem to be the case. A lack of initial confidence would, therefore, not disqualify a poverty victim, or a person otherwise to be rehabilitated, from benefiting in this respect.

The chi square figures that resulted from our analyses of *dependent* and *independent* were very similar, but the distributions were not. Correlation between the two concepts was not significant, as we anticipated it would be ($r = .24$), and, lacking a confirmed relationship, one questions whether these image-concepts were actually polar in the thinking of the respondents. *Independence,* although tending toward our prediction, might have been related in the patients' thinking to a trait, as we assumed; but *dependence* might have been related to a specific object, such as dependence on the hospital or the family. The instructions were the same for all self-images, and it was only the self-image *sick* that was altered after the first administration of the questionnaire. The discrepancy between the data for *dependent* and *independent* is most apparent when we compare the data for the short-stay group in the two tables. We could only investigate this after the fact, and with uncertain reliability.

The highly subjective self-image of being *easily hurt* is ambiguous. It might have a physical or interpersonal referent. Nevertheless, two-thirds of the respondents placed themselves in the "yes" or "no" categories. The direction is as predicted and is just short of statistical significance. We feel justified in including this self-image in the category of confirmed prediction for those patients who remained in the hospital longer than a year, or beyond the period of short-stay as defined.

Hard-working, a concept that might be a hallmark of the rehabilitation hospital, yielded non-significant results. It seems that most patients believed that they were at least average or hard workers in all categories of hospital stay. This image may not be shared by the role models, and indeed this self-image was not found to be the highest in the patient-staff congruency data. It was in the first six most congruent, as reported in the next section of the evaluation.

Likable was found to be significant for the extreme categories, and even greater significance was shown in the repeated analysis. The short-stay patients showed a fairly even distribution in their responses, and, with time, a change is evident toward a feeling of being a likable person. This same increase was not reflected in the congruence data between staff and patients so that we cannot attribute this to an exclusive influence of the role models.

Optimistic and *confident,* being two significantly increasing trait images, were positively correlated and gave us a single factor with which we could meaningfully deal in terms of the effect of the environment on the patients, but without role model support or without being attributed to the single effect of having staff members working with them. Congruency occurred, as will be shown later, on traits that did not significantly increase over time with stay in the hospital. This finding was due to: (1) the large number of "average" ratings made by the role models in rating the patients, and (2) some lack of agreement between role models in rating the patients on the traits. All role models thought that the traits were important, but one person would rate a patient one way on the trait and another person would rate the same patient differently. This material will be covered more extensively in the next section.

Suffice it to say that none of the positive shifts can be claimed to be directly related to an influence of the role models, although a general agreement between what patients thought of themselves and what the staff members thought of them increased per patient from the short-stay through the long-stay groups. This result strongly suggests that the theory of role models affecting patient progress is valid at a more global level of congruency between patients' self-assessments and staff evaluations, but not where specific traits are concerned.

Sickness, as a self-image, posed problems of interpretation. The patients gave no indication, however, of a self-image of being ill while working in the rehabilitation hospital.

The data on *slowness* are not in agreement with the hypothesized decrease. The directional trend suggests that it is a reflection of an increase in work pressure in the medium-stay period of rehabilitation, with a slackening for longer-stay patients. This comment is supported by the relatively high agreement between role models on the image as a concept that can be detected.

The final critical test, excluding the sex self-image, concerned *valuable* as an image. There is a very slight shift to twice as many long-stay patients responding positively to this trait and showing that this is a general feeling among them. We conclude that "valuableness" between patients and staff members occurs as an operating concept among many, but not uniformly among all work role relationships.

Masculinity and *femininity* were included in the questionnaire for special reasons. We wished to know whether image change along these dimensions followed the pattern of biological sex. If change was shown to occur, a shift in self-image of traits relatively distant from work would be found. Some jobs in the hospital were sex-linked in that they were usually performed by one sex or another; most of the jobs were performed by both men and women in the community, and, in the rehabilitation hospital, this was equally true. In a later section, we will show that *masculinity* was a concept both patients and role models agreed upon, and role models agreed with patients in their self-assessment. *Femininity* did not enjoy this status.

The data were not of sufficient magnitude to test by the usual chi square, but the cell tallies reveal trends. In Table B-3 the distributions for the female patients are presented. The data are reported for "yes" and "no" categories of response only, as there were few replies in the "moderate" categories.

A study of these data shows a slight tendency for the women

TABLE B-3

Distribution of Responses
as to Sex Image for Females (N = 30)

Groups	Feminine		Masculine	
	No	Yes	No	Yes
Short-stay	4	3	7	1
Medium-stay	2	4	7	1
Long-stay	1	5	5	2
Total	7	12	19	4

with longer stay in the hospital to adjudge themselves more feminine, as predicted. A surprising number of female patients did not note *feminine* as their self-image in the short-stay group. A slight increase in *masculine* was found in the long-stay group. Hazarding a guess as to the reason for this result, we may conclude that it is due to the relatively unsupervised nature of the work in the shop where this group was employed and this factor produced a feeling of masculinity. There were also more men than women in the shop of long-stayers.

The same type of data is shown for the men in Table B-4.

TABLE B-4

Distribution of Responses
as to Sex Image for Males (N = 42)

Groups	Feminine		Masculine	
	No	Yes	No	Yes
Short-stay	6	3	3	3
Medium-stay	9	3	4	2
Long-stay	7	3	5	7
Total	22	9	12	12

It is not until the category of long-stay that we find a shift toward categorization of response as predicted: greater *masculine*, less *feminine* for the males. These results lend support to the prediction of change toward a self-image more concomitant with the biological sex. The change is not progressive throughout hospitalization in the new environment; it is more likely to come later than earlier in the process. Table B-1 has shown data that do not support the notion that the rehabilitation program makes men more masculine and women more feminine.

No patients rated themselves both *masculine and feminine,* showing that they were cognizant of the meanings of the traits. Four short-stay patients, one medium, and one long-stay patient marked "no" on both traits. Five short-stay, one medium, and no long-stay patients marked "about average" on both traits. These results indicate a growing awareness of differentiation and might well be the most significant results of this part of the investigation. There were other observations worthy of note: many of the male patients rated themselves as not *feminine* but "average" on *masculinity*. This type of response was most noticeable among the short- and medium-stay men. Almost without exception, those women who were working in the community, or living in the hostel and doing domestic chores, marked themselves *feminine* and not *masculine,* as opposed to those who were in the same long-stay group and who were working in the workshops alongside men. This latter group tended to mark themselves "average" on *feminine* and "no" on *masculine.* The consistency of this result brings in the importance of rehabilitation hospital assignment as a mediating experience to change self-image. It was quite possible that the more "feminine" women were selected or otherwise brought about their assignments in domestic duties. As a check of this possibility, the repeated ratings of those women in the short-stay group who had changed their assignments to housekeeping or domestic chores and those who still remained in the workshops were studied. The shift toward *feminine,* which is noted later in this section, occurred for all the women whose assignments had been changed.

The remaining self-image traits were analyzed and six were found worthy of brief discussion. Although the distributions varied on some of them, most, such as *happy, clean, kind, refined, obedient, sincere,* and *understanding,* were answered affirmatively throughout the groups; others were answered negatively: *suspicious, stingy, stubborn, loud, greedy, critical, bossy, conceited, scheming, complaining,* and *angry.* We should note that these traits are usually answered in this way as socially desirable by normal subjects. There was no tendency for the patients to rate themselves unrealistically positive, as has been found by other investigators among some schizophrenic patients (Kamano, 1964), because many of these ratings were placed in the "moderate" categories.

The change in the concepts *broad-minded* and *religious* were not significant but showed a tendency toward an equal distribution throughout the groups and categories of response.

The data for the analyses of *absent-minded, brave, intelligent, moody, neat,* and *strong* were especially interesting in their significance, not only statistically but also by the implications the results had on the effect of the program on the patients. These results are also included in the summary Table B-2.

Absent-minded was, curiously, the most significant of our findings. The effect of the environment with the pressure of remunerative work produces a person who feels himself more able to recall various activities and items associated with the job. This could be a source of great personal satisfaction to the patient (and to the poverty victim). It may have the general effect of making the institutionalized person feel that he is more intelligent than formerly, which was shown to have been the case with our sample. The two images may, therefore, be psychologically related.

Half of the recently admitted patients thought themselves "average." A quarter considered themselves not *intelligent,* and another quarter marked themselves *intelligent.* Of course, this is a relative matter, which depends greatly on the patients' experiences and education, but the patients in these groups were not significantly different in tested intelligence and intelligence was not one of the basic factors that affected progress in the program. No grossly unintelligent patients were represented in the sample, but there was a significant change despite these considerations.

Less *absent-minded* and more *intelligent* were analyzed separately as they were marked by the patients and a distinct relationship existed ($r_s = .72$). This was not true of the other self-image traits.

The image of being *brave* is of highly dubious theoretical value and the concept may connote many meanings. Some patients expressed the feeling that it was brave of them to venture forth into the community after long years in the hospital. Nevertheless, there was significance established.

An equal initial distribution became more positive, then negative, and indicated an environmental effect to the detriment of the long-term patient who remains in the rehabilitation program.

Another self-image, similar to *brave,* is *strong.* These are socially approved attributes, especially among men. The data for *strong* revealed a directional shift significantly different from *brave* and, as even more socially sought after, *strength* was shared by the majority of the short-stay patients. This self-image diminished with stay in the hospital.

As a self-image, being *clean* was a trait shared by most patients regardless of group: 37 said "yes," three said "no." The very similar trait of being *neat* was one that became less positive with time.

In discussing "norm-receiving" as a social psychological phenomenon in Chapter 7, we suggested that such norms as neatness depend upon the demands of the situation. The distribution pertaining to neatness verifies that this is what occurs and that the patients become less homogeneous in their perception of themselves regarding this self-image, because of the influence of the various work roles that are imposed on them.

The last trait for which we will offer a data analysis in Table B-2 is *moody.* The test was not significant, but the data show a trend that supports the assumption that environment does affect self-images in this area.

The testing of the short-stay patients was done as a cross-validation of the findings. These patients were tested with the minor changes mentioned earlier. These new data failed to reach the level of the data for the medium-stay group, but significant changes were noted when appropriate tests were performed (McNemar Test for the Significance of Changes, Siegel, 1956) with the short-stay patients serving as their own control.

There was a shift toward more *active* (not significant), increase in *anxious* (not significant), more *confident* (significant, $p <$ .05), no essential change in *dependent,* but a significant change toward *independent* ($p < .01$). *Easily hurt* showed a significant shift toward the negative response (p < .05) as found previously. There was no significance shown in the remaining self-image traits: *hard-working, likable, valuable, sick,* but a tendency for *optimistic, slow* in the predicted direction; and the men failed to see themselves as more *masculine,* but the women shifted their responses to more *feminine* (p < .05). The numbers were so small as to be indeterminate where the sexual data were concerned. With these additional tests we are justified in concluding, however, that the general thesis of a predicted change was confirmed concerning some significant areas.

Congruence was defined as measured agreement between staff members and patients. The measure of congruence was the mean agreement for all the patients in one of the three specific groups, short-stay, medium-stay, and long-stay, between their self-image and those of two staff nurses rating them independently.

First, a word of explanation must be included about the inter-judge agreements. Four sets of judges rated the patients in four units. These judges were considered to be work role models for and by the patients, that is, they were considered to be valuable sources of aid in the work that the patients were performing. There was 44.0 per cent agreement between the judges in the intake unit workshop, 57.7 per cent agreement between judges in a workshop somewhat higher in the rehabilitation progression, 56.8 per cent agreement among the judges in the unit preceding discharge, and the greatest agreement, 68.7 per cent, in the unit where the most regressed patients worked. This finding suggests that, allowing for the difference in the judges, the more deteriorated the patient and the more routine the work, the greater agreement to be expected. A patient whose improvement is slight might be easier to evaluate. The data pertaining to the work reports reported in Appendix A, however, do not bear this out, and the improvement of these patients from a very low level appears related to greater inter-judge agreement.

Only the data based upon the traits where the models agreed fully with one another were used in the analysis. Irrespective of group, there was no significant difference in the congruence between judgments by staff and subjects, whether male or female (respective means, 43.5 per cent congruence; 42.8 per cent congruence).[3] There were significant differences between groups in the predicted direction although, as shown by the range of congruence, the variation was also great. The long-stay, for example, could not be considered to be homogeneous with the short- and medium-stay groups. The means and ranges of congruence were: short-stay mean: 38.46 per cent (range: 14 to 86 per cent); medium-stay mean: 46.33 per cent (range: 19 to 64 per cent); long-stay mean: 51.14 per cent (range: 28 to 88 per cent).

The linear time since admission for the patients against self-image congruence was plotted, and the correlation was found between these variables. This procedure presented a clearer picture of congruence progression. The rank order correlation was not significant, and the plot showed that the high congruence in the long-stay group was, in terms of stay in the hospital/factory, closer to the medium-stay group. The clustering of highest congruence was among those patients who had been in the rehabilitation hospital from eleven months to one year, nine months. Only three of the patients admitted in the more recent period had congruence over 50 per cent, whereas eight patients had 50 per cent or more congruence during the eleven month to one year, nine month period. Five of the relatively long-stay patients had a higher than 50 per cent congruence. None of these patients were over the 70 per cent mark.

These results indicated that congruence between models' and patients' self-image, in the form we assessed, was progressive up to a point, but did not include the patients who remained in the hospital for over two years, six months. We omitted for further analysis those patients who were beyond this point in their stay from the long-stay group. We determined that congruence was significantly related (by a separate correlation) to period of time in the hospital for those patients in the environment less than two years, six months ($r_s = .435$, df 53, $p < .01$). Ratings became more accurate between

---

[3] The congruence percentages refer to the number of traits marked the same on the continuum by the patients as by the staff member asked to rate them.

patients and patients and staff if the patient remained in the hospital up to this point.

We investigated the cases of the patients in the long-stay group as revised and found that two had been returned to the parent hospital and three had been discharged to open employment. The congruence means for the two returnees were 26 per cent and 24 per cent. The means for the working patients were 36 per cent, 61 per cent, and 54 per cent. This difference for a relatively small group is important, for it shows a tendency for the patients with higher congruence to be placed outside the hospital, while those of lower congruence had a tendency to be returned for further treatment. Needless to say, other factors were immediately involved, and the congruence was unknown by those who arranged the disposition of these patients.

The assumption that long-stay patients would show more realistic occupational expectations than short-stay patients was not borne out by the data. When unrealistic expectancies were analyzed, significantly more short-stay patients than long-stay patients had these, according to our sorting list ($p < .05$). However, there was considerable variation in the short-stay group. This variation was obvious throughout the analyses and may be attributed in part to the fact that these patients came from a variety of other hospitals. It is necessary to assume that different parent hospital environments produced different types of expectancies.

There was likewise no significant difference in the number of future expectations between the groups, but the tendency for a greater number of the short-stay patients to have more future expectations than the long-stay patients was pronounced, but not significant ($p < .20$).

The most significant difference found ($p < .01$) was in terms of the "don't know" responses in the sortings when present expectation of themselves and rehabilitation hospital expectations were combined. The mean for the long-stay group was 4.0; the mean for the short-stay group was 10.3. This result confirmed our assumption that the newly admitted patient was much more uncertain of his role in the rehabilitation hospital than his long-stay counterpart.

The responses of the short-stay patients did not show more

affiliation with the mental patient reference group and thus failed to confirm this assumption. There was a tendency (not significant) for the long-stay patients to show greater mean affiliation with this reference group. This was a reversal of our prediction when the means of affiliation for each are compared statistically. It was found upon subsequent analysis that this result was due to the selection of responses as the data, rather than selection of the category of patients as respondents.

Significantly greater affiliation was shown among the long-stay patients with the rehabilitation hospital reference group (p < .05). In other words, these data treated in this way yielded the results that the long-stay patients as a group identified with both rehabilitation hospital and general mental patient as reference groups to a greater extent than did the short-stay group. The data for the short-stay group between present expectation for both mental patient and rehabilitation hospital affiliation were not independent. When mental patient affiliation and rehabilitation hospital affiliation sortings were compared separately for this group alone, the analysis indicated that the short-stay patients felt that there was more expected of the mental patient in the ordinary mental hospital than in the rehabilitation hospital. The uncertainty of the role model, as shown in the "don't know" sortings when questions regarding the rehabilitation hospital were asked, was reflected in this result.

It should be pointed out that the short-stay patients used the "don't know" choice of sorting significantly more often throughout the trials than the long-stay patients. The mean of this category of response for the long-stay patients was 9.5, and for the short-stay patients it was 17.1 (p < .05).

Our unit of measurement for the tests reported here was the affirmative sortings of responses to the sentence stems. Stephenson (1953) points out in his early work that, in correlating persons rather than tests, results can be demonstrated that show different ways of "behaving" in the experimental situation. These ways of "behaving" can be attributed to groups of persons in different categories. We found that this was true in the results of this study and accounted for the wide disparity within groups. A small number of short-stay patients, for example, tended to sort in such a way that showed they felt that very little was expected of them as the "typical" mental patient, whereas in all other sortings, that is, in expectations now and in the future, by themselves and by the rehabilitation hospital staff, considerably more was expected of them. Among these short-stay patients there was a paucity of responses showing affiliation with the mental patient as such. The data suggested that this group was indeed small and that, taking the patients rather than the number of responses as data, it would be found that more short-stay patients than long-stay patients had matched sortings that showed an identification with the mental patients' role. A Mann-Whitney U test was used in this analysis (Siegel, 1956). The short-stay and long-stay patients were compared, and the short-stay patients as a group were found to be ranked significantly higher on mental patient affiliation ($U = 116$, $p < .05$; $n_1 = 16$). Likewise, if the category of the patient is taken as the unit of measurement, the short-stay patients comprised the category of patients with greater present expectation and mental patient reference group congruence more often than the long-stay patients. This discrepancy between two different ways of analyzing the data was due to the very low mental patient affiliation of a small number of short-stay patients who constituted a unique group. The data support the expectation that the newly admitted *patient* shows greater affiliation with the mental patient reference group than with the reference group of the rehabilitation hospital.

Why these few short-stay patients were predisposed to denying anything to be expected from the "typical" mental patient was an enigma, until we found that all but one, that is, four, had originated from the same parent hospital, and that this was the only obvious characteristic they had in common. This observation suggested to us the importance of the hospital milieu and presumably environmental poverty milieu in forming expectations in rehabilitation.

Returning to the discussion of unrealistic-realistic expectations, we found it heartening to discover how consistently many of the patients differentiated between these sets of expectancies. Most of the unrealistic expectations scattered throughout the items in all sortings were placed in the negative section of the sorting box.

There was no significant difference in the "don't know" present expectation rehabilitation hospital sortings between male and female patients when these were separated for analysis. The respective means were 7.1 for men, and 7.3 for women. There was a tendency for the female patients to have more future expectations (with a mean of 40.8) than males (mean of 38.5), but this difference was not significant. This result may be related to an increased feeling of *femininity* among the women, over the feeling of *masculinity* among the men, because the women, feeling more feminine, could cope with more expectations in line with their sex role than men could. The result could just as well have been an artifact of the items themselves, that is, being more feminine in nature despite all efforts to reduce this factor.

The differences between the "domestic" and "emotional" items (sixteen in each category) were analyzed in terms of sorting. There was no reason to anticipate differences, and many of the items might well be loosely termed "interpersonal" and be subsumed under this title in both categories. In the present expectation sorting, as opposed to the future expectation, there was no significant difference ("domestic" mean 12.5; "emotional" mean 13.3). There was no difference in the future expectations ("domestic" mean 13.5; "emotional" mean 13.8), no difference in the rehabilitation hospital expectations ("domestic" mean 12.7; "emotional" mean 13.7), and likewise no difference in the mental patient expectations ("domestic" mean 2.24; "emotional" mean 2.25).

APPENDIX C

List of
Traits

Below is a list of terms that are used to describe people. Please tick (check) once in the spaces after the words. Think of yourself honestly before doing so, and if you don't know the word, ask what it means. If the word describes you, tick under "This describes me to a strong (or moderate) degree"; if the word does not describe you, tick under "This does not describe me at all (moderately)"; if you are about average, tick under "About average." Now go ahead and try not to put all the ticks under one column.

Absent-minded	Feminine	Refined
Active	Greedy	Religious
Angry	Happy	Scheming
Anxious	Hard-working	Sick
Brave	Independent	Sincere
Broadminded	Intelligent	Slow
Bossy	Kind	Stingy
Clean	Likable	Strong
Conceited	Loud	Stubborn
Complaining	Masculine	Suspicious
Confident	Moody	Understanding
Critical	Neat	Valuable
Dependent	Obedient	
Easily hurt	Optimistic	

Completion
Phrases

Phrases used on the reference group cards (appropriate stems are to be found in Appendix B).

. . . read newspapers

. . . keep a job for a year

. . . clean house

. . . plan a holiday

. . . be satisfied with life

. . . be happy

. . . watch television

. . . shave, dress, and wash without help

. . . have baths regularly

. . . enjoy a joke

. . . vote

. . . go to the toilet without help

. . . work as well as any other person

. . . be friendly on the job

. . . enjoy listening to people

. . . use good table manners without help

. . . have a postal savings account

. . . keep up with others in the job

. . . know about "sick notes"

. . . obey traffic signals

. . . forget being a mental patient

. . . order a dinner in a cafe

. . . telephone someone

. . . get to and from work outside hospitals

. . . be a great artist or musician

. . . earn at least £100 a week

. . . run for Parliament

. . . take care of relatives

. . . raise a family

. . . not talk to myself

. . . sleep no more than eight hours a night

. . . manage a business

. . . earn £15–20 a week

. . . not get angry

. . . earn at least £10 a week

. . . stay out of hospital

. . . fall in love

. . . play games with other people

. . . fill out a job application

. . . keep taking tablets

. . . make out income tax forms

. . . know what I (they) do most of the time

. . . cook a meal for myself

. . . speak well at an interview for a job

. . . buy food

. . . save money

. . . take a journey alone

. . . be a good mixer

. . . help someone who is injured

. . . enjoy talking

Description:
Study III

☙ MEASURES AND METHODOLOGY ❧

This study was divided into four stages: first, contructing and perfecting a three-scale questionnaire; secondly, comparing the staff members' questionnaire scores on humanistic-custodialism with their ratings of patients to determine whether their attitudes influenced their actual evaluation of patients; thirdly, extracting from a retest of the questionnaire, on a small group of nurses who had been in the hospital as staff members for a year, data with particular emphasis on change toward any one dominant orientation; and, finally, relating the orientations to the attitudes shown by the nurses.

The first stage of the inquiry took into consideration this vital aspect of mental treatment, about which there has been extensive research: the custodial-to-humanistic attitude continuum.[1]

It occurred to us that the collective position of the staff members along the continuum was determined not solely by their personality, their status in the institution, or even their work orientation, but by the extent of chronicity of the patients in the specific hospital. We believed that a tendency toward custodialism in a staff member's thinking was not always contrary to the activity of the member in his work role with the patient. This custodial viewpoint was particularly valid when the patient and staff member were performing together a common job not concerned with the patient's imminent discharge. The belief that "once a schizophrenic, always a schizophrenic," or maintaining an "organic" interpretation of the etiology of mental illness, was not contradictory to the efforts of the staff member to rehabilitate the patient to full-time employment. It is reasonable to assume that a change in the nature of the patient population from a chronically stabilized and middle-aged one to a population composed of young, acutely ill people with more florid symptoms would alter the attitude the staff had about mental illness

[1] A summary of this material was presented to the staff of the rehabilitation hospital in a printed report, August, 1964. The same material, which was entitled "Analysis of Staff Questionnaire," is incorporated in this Appendix.

in general. Direct experience influences attitude change more than any single factor.

The measure used for our assessment was a seven-point, twenty-item scale called the *Custodial Mental Illness Scale,* or CMI (Gilbert and Levinson, 1957). This scale was chosen because comparative data on this scale were easily obtained for hospitals in both the United States and England. The scores derived from the scale range from 10 to 70. A lower score means more humanistic beliefs, such as optimism regarding basic personality change of the patient; a higher score means more custodial beliefs, or a more pessimistic view of any permanent change. In the reference (Gilbert and Levinson, 1957) scores are reported for different types of hospitals. Some were designed to serve a chronic patient population with little occupational and rehabilitative work being done and others were designed for an acute patient population with work similar to that of the rehabilitation hospital.

The hospitals were, by description: (1) a small (150 beds) state institution for active treatment of acute cases (CMI score = 29.0, N = 109); (2) a large (1800 beds) Veterans Administration hospital for a "mixed bag" of patients (CMI score = 32.9, N = 111); (3) a large state institution for chronic patients (CMI score = 33.7, N = 115); (4) a specialized rehabilitation unit for acute cases, not all psychotic (CMI score = 22.9, N = 10); (5) the rehabilitation hospital for chronic patients (CMI score = 32.8, N = 52). These data indicate that the staffs of hospitals treating acute cases have lower CMI scores than the staffs of hospitals treating chronic cases. We, of course, had no way of determining the exact data regarding chronicity and relied only on the descriptions of the hospitals.

The range of scores at the rehabilitation hospital was from 13 to 50.5, representing a wide variety of opinions. The average for the other hospitals was 31.3, with a range from 15 to 52. It is not only the type of patients, as shown by these comparisons, that creates a difference in the direction of the scores but the presence or absence of professional training of the staff. When the forty-one psychiatrically trained staff (nurses, social workers, psychiatrists) were separated from the eleven untrained staff (such as secretaries, aides, and engineers), the data obtained were similar to the data reported in the published research. The mean for the trained staff members was 31.4 and for the untrained staff was 36.7 (t = 2.43, 50 df, p < .05). Data were also collected on the time actually spent with the patients in the working day (no part-time staff members were included). The mean was lower but not significantly so (t = 1.08, 50 df, p < .05) for those who noted that they spend more than thirty hours with patients: 32.3 (N = 30); less than thirty hours: 34.6 (N = 22). Most but not all of these former staff members were trained. Data were obtained on the extent of vis-à-vis contact with patients, zero to five hours a week, five to ten hours a week, ten to twenty hours, and twenty to thirty hours. There was no consistent relationship between these categories and the CMI scores.

Our conclusions, where staff attitudes were concerned, were that (a) at a molar level of analysis, the chronicity of the patient in the hospital was related to feelings among the staff toward patients *en masse,* and (b) this was only slightly dependent upon the extent of actual working contact, as in the work role relationship.

The scale (Appendix F) was devised in the following way: (1) We accumulated as many statements as possible that were pertinent to one "orientation" or another. The source of these statements was the observations we had made of the rehabilitation hospital in operation. (2) We asked three judges to separate the statements according to the three categories and only those that were the least ambiguous and that all three judges agreed represented the attitude universe were used. We defined a "professional orientation" as a focus in thinking and action on one's career and placing professional advancement before other considerations. We defined a "patient orientation" as a focus in thinking and action on the care and treatment of the individual patient, not merely following general professional practice but actively seeking out the patient to extend help. We defined a "production orientation" as a focus in thinking and action on the economics and ethics of fulfilling production contracts and quotas and building trade above all other considerations. (3) The five-point scale statements were given to a small number of staff members (fourteen). We performed an item analysis and correlated the scores of the individual items within the scales (from one, or "strongly disagree," to five, or "strongly agree") with the between scores on that item and the total scores obtained on all items in the separate "orientation" scales. (4) Only those items that were significantly intercorrelated and discriminating in this way were used in the scales, and were felt to be sufficiently divorced from other items for inclusion. (5) We collated the separate scales into one questionnaire for presentation.

Our research questionnaire consisted of forty-five items—fifteen items in each separate "orientation." The separate scale items were randomized and the direction of response categories was alternated in the finished questionnaire. Upon interrogation, we found that some items were still ambiguous, but we felt that the questionnaire was the best that we could have formulated under the circumstances, where a small number of staff served as both pilot and experimental group.

Signifying agreement to an opinion does not determine a course of action entirely consistent with the stated opinion, as social scientists investigating prejudice well know. We sought a method of checking our orientational results. The respondents were asked, as an addendum to the questionnaire, to note which course of action, from a choice of four, they would take in specific situations; they also had the option of responding "don't know." This was called the "situational test," and there were three situations presented to the respondents. These situations can be thought of as conflicts of interest and were constructed to be as real as possible to the routine operation of the rehabilitation hospital. The first situation described a conflict between the "patient orientation"—counseling a patient at an awkward time—and the "production orientation"—continuing an important aspect of the job in the workshop. The second situation contrasted a "professional orientation"—attending a technical movie on nursing practice—with a "production orientation"—dealing with the delivery of material to the hospital from one of the subcontract agents. The last situation was concerned with the remaining possibility, that is, "patient" vs. "professional orientation," and the respondent had the choice of continuing an individual relationship felt to be of extreme importance to a patient, or accepting another, more attractive, post. We do not pretend that the conflicts engendered in these situations are of equal magnitude.

A member of the staff later pointed out that the desired effect of the last situation was somewhat mitigated by the fact that strong involvement with patients was not emphasized in the training in the teaching hospitals from which the nurses of the group originated, and in some hospitals, such involvement was discouraged. This does not mean that nurse-patient involvement does not occur in a hospital of the size and type of the rehabilitation hospital.

The choices ranged from "don't know" to both directions signifying full endorsement by the respondents' actions in accord with one orientation or another. An opportunity for a partial endorsement was given between the extremes.

◄§ RESULTS AND DISCUSSION §►

The orientation scales were of the same length, and the scores had the possible range from one to seventy-five. The mean for "professional orientation" in the sample was 51.36, range 39 to 64; mean for "patient orientation" was 54.61, range 46 to 70; mean for "production orientation" was 45.71, range 31 to 62. The differences between these scale scores were significant (two-tailed tests, $p < .05$), with the exception of the differences between "professional" and "patient orientation." We conclude that "patient orientation" was more strongly endorsed than "production orientation." This is all the more interesting occurring as it does in the hospital/factory, where production is the *prima facie* orientation of the staff in their work through the daily routine of the hospital.

First, we wished to know if the scores differentiated between role models who were all greatly involved, that is, more than thirty hours a week, with patients, and particularly in the separate workshops, in the clinic, or on night duty. The analysis of variance was applied in a three-by-six design (three measures on six groups in different areas of the hospital). The analysis of these data appears in Table E-1.

Brief inspection of these results shows that differences between the separate orientations differentiated the work areas. The scale

TABLE E-1

Analysis of Variance of Scale Scores:
Work Areas vs. Orientation

Source of Variation	SS	df	MS	F
Between Areas:	557.715	2	278.857	4.416*
Between Staff				
Same Area:	1704.985	27	63.146	
Total Between Staff:	2262.7	29		
Between Scales:	1588.26	2	794.130	30.473**
Interaction:				
Scales Area	193.134	10	19.313	.074
Interaction:				
Staff Scales	1406.806	48	26.060	
Total Within Staff:	3188.2	60		
Total:	5450.9	89		

* p < .05
** p < .01

means differed even more. There was essentially no interaction between the scores on the three scales and the unit area in which the staff member worked. We can now compare the separate means, assured that they differ on the two variables independently.

In Table E-2 are shown data as they pertain to the various sections of the hospital where the nursing staff worked.[2] In Chapter 3 the intake unit and chronic unit were known by their designated color names, Grey and Blue respectively.

It is interesting to note that the highest "production orientation" occurs in the middle unit, where the push for production may be greatest before the patient is "graduated" to the more loosely supervised discharge unit. In the latter unit, the patients work free of supervision to a considerable extent and a "patient orientation" tends to predominate among the staff and at the same level as in

[2] Selecting these areas as working units does not in any sense mean that other areas are not working units as well. The reason for selecting these was twofold: (a) the number of staff in these units was sufficient for analysis, and (b) they constituted areas where the staff worked in close relationship with one another and shared ideas related to the orientations. Excluded from the units were those staff members in the Domestic Section, Clerical Section, gardeners, and such.

TABLE E-2

Means of Orientation Scores
According to Respondents' Work Area

		Orientations		
Area	N	Prof.	Pt.	Prod.
Intake	7	48.3	52.4	43.9
Chronic	4	47.75	54.0	44.0
Middle	5	50.2	60.6	55.42
Discharge	4	55.25	60.0	46.75
Clinic	6	52.7	53.7	44.3
Night	5	56.2	60.2	47.0
	31			

the middle unit. These results are consistent with expectations based upon the structure of the hospital factory. What is not so easily explained is the night staff data showing a relatively high "production orientation" compared with this orientation in other sections, although it is the lowest orientation among the three scales. There is little opportunity for production to be accomplished among the night staff, although this aspect of the hospital's operation may be widely discussed in their nocturnal rounds. This group showed a high mean orientation toward the individual patient, which is understandable. The "patient orientation" emphasis was not reflected among the clinic staff, which seems strange. A strong "patient orientation" in the intake unit is not surprising, for it is in this unit that much of the initial evaluation of patients is done. This orientation fails to reach the proportions of those staff members in the discharge unit, middle unit, and of those having night duties.

Situational Tests

The situational part of the assessment was replete with improbabilities, so that complete agreement between a staff member's orientation and his responses to the situations was not anticipated. As a validity measure, the situational test was used to determine to what extent the staff members' endorsement of the statements on the scales was mirrored in his reactions to certain critical incidents. If his "professional orientation" scale score was greater than his "patient orientation" scale score, and his professional feelings dominated over his feelings toward the patient in the situation, it would be concluded that the two types of assessments were in agreement. Disagreement would be found where these score results and the results from the situation test were in opposition. Needless to say, if "profession" was less than "patient," and the same was found in the situation test, agreement would be found. Each of the fifty-two sets of data were analyzed in this way: the "profession-patient" combination was found to conform in 35 per cent of the cases, due to the unlikelihood of the situation occurring in experience as will be mentioned in more detail. The "patient-production" combination was in agreement in 92 per cent of the sets, and the "profession-production" combination was in agreement in 61 per cent of the sets.

We had reason to believe that the scales were not completely valid when we analyzed the data in Table E-2, finding, as we did, that those staff members in the units most concerned with the products of the hospital failed to have relatively high "production" scores; and finding, likewise, that those staff members having most to do with the patients *sans* productive work having relatively low "patient" scores. This is not as justifiable a test as the procedure described above because (a) to a limited extent, there were occasional staff shifts between the clinic and the unit, and (b) the training of all staff members working in these areas of the rehabilitation hospital tended to be very similar in the various teaching hospitals represented.

First, the results in terms of which orientation predominated after dichotomizing the situational test response categories are reported. Table E-3 shows the results for the sample of fifty-two staff members with the data for those respondents who marked "don't know" on any situation extracted.

If each situation is treated independently, tests of significance can be applied as a series of one-sample cases between each of the "orientation" categories. The results of these tests for the "patient-production orientation" was $\chi^2 = 43.2$ in favor of the "patient orientation" being the higher, and for the "profession-patient orientation," $\chi^2 = 33.8$ in favor of the "profession orientation" being the

TABLE E-3

Frequencies of Orientation Domination
On Situation Test for All Staff (N = 52)

Orientations	Frequencies*
Pt > Prof	3
Pt > Prod	49
Prof > Pt	42
Prof > Prod	30
Prod > Pt	2
Prod > Pt	21

* In a very few cases Ss failed to respond.

higher. Both of these results were significant (p < .001). The data analysis of the "profession-production orientation" was not significant ($\chi^2 = 1.56$).

The results give a clear picture of a staff predominantly "patient oriented" over "production," but "professionally oriented" over both "production" and "patient." Some of the intermediary choices in the response categories gave latitude in caring for the interests of the workshop, and the movie situation could also be interpreted indirectly as "patient oriented" in the Prof > Prod–Prod > Prof conflict. In this way, the Pt > Prod result might even be more significantly directed toward patients. In general, these results substantiated the profession first, patient second, and production last alignment in the thinking of the staff.

Without a topical checklist it is difficult to substantiate whether one orientation or another dominated staff interaction. The topics seemed to be related to time and place as the routine of the day's activity unfolded, "professionally-oriented" topics being discussed during breaks in the work, "patient-oriented" topics occurring during more formal meetings, and "production-oriented" topics transpiring on the workshop floor.

The data from the situation test were analyzed according to the staff units. Table E-4 shows these data.

The intake, chronic, and night staff units, the middle and discharge units have comparable number of choices represented because of missing data. The middle unit again shows a generally

TABLE E-4

Frequencies of Orientation Domination on Situation Test
According to Respondents' Work Area for Selected Staff (N = 31)

				Areas			
Orientations	In-take	Chronic	Middle	Dis-charge	Clinic	Night	Total
Pt > Prof	1	1	0	0	1	1	4
Pt > Prod	4	4	3	3	5	4	23
Prof > Pt	4	3	3	3	4	3	20
Prof > Prod	3	4	0	2	4	2	15
Prod > Pt	0	0	0	0	0	0	0
Prod > Prof	0	0	3	1	1	2	7

high degree of "production orientation"; the "patient orientation" of the discharge unit is not so apparent as in the questionnaire results. There is essentially no difference between the intake and chronic units. We have a second time shown the slight "production" emphasis among the night staff, although the "patient orientation" predominates. No section of the nursing staff indicated a "production orientation" exceeding "patient orientation."

Another way of showing the predominance of "patient orientation" among the members of the collective hospital staff is through a reporting of the percentages of responses arranged along the continua. Below is a brief one-sentence précis of the three situations followed by the response categories. We see that dichotomization of the data presents a distorted picture of complete orientation in any one direction. The difficulty presented by the last situation as compared with the first two situations is depicted in the many "don't know" responses. These "don't know" responses indicated that the last situation was one the respondents thought unlikely to occur.

The inferences we have made from the results thus far are far removed from the specific questions that made up the content of the questionnaire.

One original question remains unanswered: Are these independent orientations related to a general custodial or humanistic approach to patients? It would be reasonable to assume that an inverse relationship (significance at $p < .05$) would be obtained be-

1. Patient asks to see you at a busy time in the workshop.

Finish the job, or "production orientation"		Don't Know	Talk with patient privately, or "patient orientation"	
0	4%	0	63%	33%

2. Van arrives when you are about to go to a professional movie.

Go to movie, or "professional orientation"		Don't Know	Help driver, or "production orientation"	
4%	54%	0	23%	19%

3. You have the opportunity for a better paying job meaning that you will have to break off with a dependent patient.

Stay with patient, or "patient orientation"		Don't Know	Go to job, or "professional orientation"	
0	6%	14%	42%	38%

tween "patient orientation" scores and high CMI scores, a positive relationship between "production" and this measure, and no relationship between "profession" and the measure. One would predict that the humanistic approaches and an emphasis on the product manufactured in the rehabilitation hospital would be antithetical.

The correlations were not significant for "patient orientation" ($r_s = .25$, 50 df, $p < .10$); not significant for "profession orientation" ($r_s = .19$, 50 df, $p < .05$); and significant for "production orientation" ($r_s = .37$, 50 df, $p < .01$). These results support the hypothesis of a positive association between "production orientation" and custodialism. A tendency toward a positive relationship, rather than an inverse relationship, was found between "patient orientation" and a humanistic approach. A possible explanation of this result rests with the philosophy of custodialism unique to the rehabilitation hospital. We have conjectured that the chronicity of the patient may be an important variable in determining the CMI scores. We must consider the possibility that custodialism is not in disagreement with the rehabilitation process as it is envisoned by the staff of the rehabilitation hospital. We will have further confirmation of this idea when we examine the data on attitude change among the role model staff members.

Change in Attitude

Central to our thesis is the notion that staff attitudes alter as an effect of working in the environment of the hospital. The test of opinion change was conducted among a select number of the nursing staff members, the role models, who joined the staff during the first six months of the research study and who were available for retesting at the end. Two men who were at the hospital for training were retested after only six weeks. The average time between testings was thirty-one weeks. Although all orientation scores increased, the greatest increase was found in the "production orientation." The amount of increase varied: "professional orientation," +5.5; "patient orientation," +5.0; "production orientation," +8.5. There was no difference in the amount of increase between the durations of stay in the hospital program.

There was also an increase in the CMI scores in the direction of greater custodialism: +6.75. Custodialism did not increase among the two students who worked for a shorter period of time. The scores for a control group $(N = 10)$ tested and retested at a nearby psychiatric hospital were essentially the same. Before any conclusions can be drawn from these results, much more investigation is required. These data suggest, however, an increase in custodialism with lengthy experience in the rehabilitation hospital.

We compared, with their CMI scores, the responses of the staff members who were tested after the longer time to the statement: "I have changed my beliefs (from custodial to humanistic ones) about patients since I have been working with mental patients." In all but one case their scores became more custodial despite their affirmative replies to the statement, which suggests that it was unknown to the subjects themselves.

Which statements on the CMI scale showed an increase in scores? Averaging the changes, we found that the following statements showed an increase of at least four points, or over half of the points allowable on the continuum:

1. Only a person with considerable psychiatric training should be allowed to form close relationships with patients.

2. As soon as a person shows signs of mental disturbance he should be hospitalized.

3. We can make some improvements, but by and large the conditions of mental hospital wards are about as good as they can be considering the type of disturbed patient living there.

4. Abnormal people are ruled by their emotions; normal people by their reason.

5. Patients need the same kind of control and discipline as untrained children.

The following two statements showed a change in the opposite, or more humanistic, direction:

1. It is best to prevent the more disturbed patients from mixing with those who are less sick.

2. With few exceptions most patients haven't the ability to tell right from wrong.

Statements one and four refer to a need for better understanding of mental patients and reflect the conclusion made that some members of the rehabilitation hospital staff feel inadequate in this area. Statement two reflects the philosophy of early treatment, and this philosophy appears to become polarized with experience in the rehabilitation hospital. Statements three and five involve the living conditions and psychological environment of the mental patient. Comparing the nature of these statements with those that showed a humanistic change, we conclude that experience in the rehabilitation hospital teaches the staff member that the psychological milieu is more important than the physical comfort of the patient in rehabilitating him. He concurs with the "clinic idea" of separating the "sick" from the "well" patients. Patients should be allowed more freedom of decision-making, but within the structured situation of explicit training by the staff of the hospital. Analyzed in this way, these changes express the ideology of the rehabilitation hospital quite well.

Staff Attitudes and Work Scores

We associated the work report data with the attitude scores obtained from the various employees who made out the reports in order to answer the question of the effect of attitude on the assessment of the patients.

Different patients, different time intervals, and staff members from different units complicated the task, but data were obtained from reports that had been scored by four individual staff members in the workshop units, and during the same interval on the same patient. Only those staff members who worked closely with the patients were included: four from the intake unit, four from the chronic unit, four from the middle unit, and four from the discharge unit. These employees had already been found to differ in their orientational scores. Although in a few cases more than two patients had been rated by these staff members in each of the units during the same interval, two patients were chosen to make the numbers comparable between units. The ratings were done independently at different periods by the raters but the time intervals between the ratings were the same.

Independent correlations were computed between the "profession orientation" scores, for example, these being four in number in a particular unit, and the work report scores given the same two patients in that unit, these being eight in number, or two sets of four.

The results of our investigation appear in Table E-5. We wished to determine if there was an association between the work report scores given patients and the attitudinal scores made by the nurses on separate units so that correlations are reported for each unit, for each attitudinal score (CMI and orientations) and for each patient.

The consistently low and sometimes inverse coefficients between the variables suggest that there is very little association between a staff member's attitudes toward his work and mental illness, and the scores he gives them for their performance. Significant relationships were obtained where we might expect to find them, that is, between the "production orientation" of the middle unit and the "patient orientation" of the discharge unit. These results strongly support our contention that orientation does affect work report scores to a slight extent, but dependent upon the feelings prevailing among the staff members in a given unit. We should not overesti-

Table E-5

Correlations Between Orientation, CMI Scores and Work Report
Scores on Four Sets of Two Patients by Sixteen Unit Staff Members

		Intake		Chronic		Middle		Discharge	
		A*	B*	A	B	A	B	A	B
	Prof.	.09	−.14	.25	.37	.30	.26	.36	.49
Scales	Pt.	.57	.52	.48	.68	.12	.35	.91ª	.78
	Prod.	.79	.67	.33	.20	.95ª	.90ª	.44	.41
	CMI	−.23	.02	.16	.22	.68	.47	−.31	−.52

* A and B denote individual patients.
ª Significant, $p < .05$, 2 df.

mate this relationship in these two exceptions because of the undetermined reliability of the instruments. We should also not lose sight
of the fact that, even though the work reports were done during the
same period of the patients' performance, the staff members worked
different shifts in some cases and this may have been a source of
variance. A patient's performance may alter during the day, or the
staff member's rating performance may differ between shifts.

# *APPENDIX F*

Staff
Questionnaire

The items appear below as they were arranged for administration.
Scale orientations are given with the items.

1. I would like to know more about how my personality affects
   patients. (Patient)
2. There are sometimes too many meetings to attend in a hospital
   of this kind. (Profession)
3. I have changed my beliefs (from custodial to humanistic ones)
   about working with patients since I have been working with
   them. (Patient)
4. There should be a greater number of production facilities just
   like St. Wulstan's for the chronic patients. (Production)
5. One can never know enough about a patient. (Patient)
6. Some sort of uniform (blazer, cap, etc.) is a must for an employee in my job at the hospital. (Profession)
7. When it comes down to it, you have to push some patients to
   get things done. (Production)
8. There need to be definite ranks among employees in any hospital so that everyone knows his responsibilities. (Profession)
9. The patient, as a person, is my primary interest. (Patient)
10. Idle hands produce unhealthy minds. (Production)
11. I tend to take the patients' problems home with me. (Patient)
12. Following a prescribed code of ethics is essential in any profes-
    sion. (Profession)
13. Above all other considerations, work, no matter what one's abil-
    ity or impairment, is a social responsibility. (Production)
14. I would feel no guilt at all in taking a patient out of the work-
    shop several hours if I felt it would benefit him. (Patient)
15. It is necessary for an employee to read during working hours as
    many journals as available to keep up with the literature in his
    profession. (Profession)
16. I feel that patient promotion to a more advanced unit should
    depend primarily on the amount of work he does. (Production)
17. I believe that the existence of refresher courses brings increased
    standing to a field or profession in the eyes of the public. (Pro-
    fession)
18. It is better for a patient to spend most of his time with staff such

as ourselves rather than be placed with patients throughout his treatment. (Patient)

19. Research would better be directed toward job performance of patients than diagnosis. (Production)

20. Education in my type of employment is more important than most people think it is. (Profession)

21. To know and handle a patient's motivation and fears is the most important job for a person working in a mental hospital. (Patient)

22. The work performance of patients is the best single indicator of a well-run hospital. (Production)

23. It is very important to know what an employee's degree or diploma initials mean. (Profession)

24. I tend to think first of a patient's particular job in the hospital when I meet him on the street rather than any other single thing about him. (Production)

25. It is very important to know how a patient will react to his Christian name, or to the use of his surname when addressing him. (Patient)

26. All patients should have the privilege of choosing the type of work that they want to do in the workshops if it is felt that they can do so. (Patient)

27. If I was asked by a young person who was selecting a career to recommend one, I would most likely suggest my type of work. (Profession)

28. How much work a patient does is more crucial for assessing him than why he does or does not do it, while he is under treatment here. (Production)

29. In an industrial workshop, any patient improvement is due more to the staff as professional people being emulated by the patient than the actual work itself. (Profession)

30. Members of the staff who eat in the staff dining room and who are at the same job should try to eat together for better communication. (Profession)

31. Products assembled in a hospital are highly important because they contribute to the national economy. (Production)

32. I would rather be in my line of work in any mental hospital than working at another job here. (Profession)

33. Many people employed in mental hospitals put their profession before helping the patients. (Patient)

34. Some jobs in the workshops appeal to me more than others in supervising patients doing them. (Production)

35. I sometimes feel that what I do scarcely helps the patients here to get out. (Patient)

36. I look forward to the visits of other workers in my profession to the hospital so that I may show them what I am doing here. (Profession)

37. We need a qualified public relations man to go into the community to sell our fabricated products, like the coat hangers. (Production)

38. I would be very unhappy to find myself so involved with administration that I would lose all patient contact. (Patient)

39. Within limits, in any mental hospital one professional worker can perform another's duties if the need arises. (Profession)

40. Our workshops would be better if we expanded the production of only those items we make ourselves. (Production)

41. My job is just like any other. (Profession)

42. The patients are like any other objects in the workshops. (Production)

43. Keeping a patient in the workshop until a job is finished before going to a class is highly permissible. (Production)

44. I believe that in our training greater patient-staff involvement should be emphasized. (Patient)

45. On every item that goes out of the hospital workshops a note "made by or assembled by mentally handicapped patients." (Patient)

Description:
Study IV

⋅ஃ MEASURES AND METHODOLOGY ঃ⋗

The design of this experiment was the traditional test-retest one with a follow-up assessment after six weeks. The patients were matched on assessment scores only; the first six groups, two groups per method, continued their instruction for twenty one-hour-long sessions, twice weekly. The first series of group members were taught by the methods, with a replication of the entire procedure, plus a control group—making seven groups in all. The remaining experimental groups were given the same material in more concentrated form for ten sessions, twice weekly. A second control group for the shorter time interval was tested. The time allotted for the material for these groups was halved but the information was more concentrated. Two control groups were used: one for twenty sessions, the other for ten sessions, with no intervening instruction. All patients were tested individually before the experiment began, on the last day of the experiment, and after six weeks.

The mean scores of the test about to be described (possible range from 0 to 60) and number of patients in the groups are shown in Table G-2 in the results section. In assigning the patients to the conditions, we matched them in fours as closely as possible, and then chose randomly for the groups. There were thirty-two men and thirty-four women in the sample of sixty-six patients, with slightly different numbers in the groups. There were no significant differences between the groups' scores ($F = 1.024$, 10 and 55 df, $p < .05$).

The Social Assessment Test

The first task was to devise an easily administered and comprehensive test that would include as much as possible of the material a rehabilitated mental patient should know. We used much of Gunzburg's material and included some other topics about which the patients' fund of knowledge had been found, through work with them at the hospital, to be deficient.

The multiple-choice format with five choices was best for our purposes because it presented the correct answer for the patient to recognize, if he could, and was similar to the tasks that would be asked of him in daily life.

The test consisted of sixty questions. There were several areas covered in six sections and the sections were arranged in such a way as to follow the patient as he "progressed" through the hospital program, applied for a job, and set up housekeeping outside the hospital.

Before a new term, such as "bank interest," was introduced in a question, it was preceded by another item asking the meaning of the appropriate word or phrase. Some items were statements with missing key words and others were questions. This variation in question format was deliberate in order to maintain patient interest.

The areas covered in the test were: (1) making a simple journey and telling time (8 items); (2) posting a letter and costs (12 items); (3) the various aspects of the Post Office's services (10 items); (4) the cost of living outside the hospital, or things one needs to know before looking for work (8 items); (5) income tax and health benefits, or things one encounters after employment (12 items); (6) use of the telephone, first aid, and miscellaneous topics (10 items).

The test was ordinarily completed in twenty to thirty minutes by the most regressed patient. The tool was called the Social Assessment Test to distinguish it from the Social Assessment and Educational Record, upon which it was based.

We related our test to the original assessment record, which categorizes patients into "satisfactory," "unsatisfactory," and "fail completely." We found nine patients in the "satisfactory" group, twenty-five in the "unsatisfactory" group, twenty-eight in the "failing completely" group—all of whom were given both types of assessments. This result showed, in itself, the extent of re-education that was needed in the hospital. There were significantly higher scores in the predicted direction between the two types of assessments ($F = 11.27$, 61 df, $p < .01$).

Association between WAIS scores and our test scores was significant for eighty-seven patients tested ($r_s = .665$, $t = 8.21$, 85 df, $p < .001$).

It appeared from the data that patients with lower IQ's had

higher scores more often than patients with higher IQ's had low scores, possibly because of the necessity of assisting several low-IQ patients take the test because some of them were illiterate. The items and choices were read to them.

There were also other factors determining the test score a patient received after admission to the rehabilitation hospital. These factors were: (1) years in the hospital from which he came ($N = 82$, $r_s = .237$, $t = 2.18$, 80 df, $p < .05$), or the more years, the lower the score; (2) the type of parent hospital ward from which he came ($N = 54$, $r_s = .20$, $t = 1.47$, 52 df, $p < .10$);[1] and (3) its diagnosis, which also was not significant ($N = 48$, schizophrenic mean, 39.19; other psychoses mean, 37.29; non-psychotic, such as inadequate personality or neurosis, mean, 37.50). Diagnosis was not related to performance on the test because intelligence and length of hospitalization were related to diagnosis, and these factors rather than type of illness alone determined the patient's performance.

A more relevant rating involved an assessment of the extent to which the newly admitted patient had enjoyed contact outside the parent hospital before coming to St. Wulstan's. Three indices were rated 0–2 and included: (1) frequency of the patient's visits to his home, (2) visits he received, and (3) parole, or town passes. Each index covered the six months immediately before admission to St. Wulstan's.

We anticipated that patients who had experienced greater community contact prior to admission would have significantly higher Assessment Test scores. The scores for *Contact with outside* were summed and ranged from 0 to 5; the mean scores of patients in these categories appear in Table G-1. A Kruskall-Wallis one-way analysis of variance on these data was not significant ($H = 3.89$, df 5, $p < .50$), (Siegel, 1956).

---

[1] The reason for the difference in number of patients in the various correlations is that some data were missing from the patients' records. A lower score on this variable denoted less restriction and this rating took into consideration twelve indices (scored 0–2) such as how often the ward was locked, the presence of airing courts, whether the patients handled their own clothing, and curfew times. The Physician Superintendent, on his visit to the parent hospital (see Chapter 3), completed the scale on several patients before their admission to the rehabilitation hospital.

TABLE G-1

Means of Assessment Test Scores
According to *Contact with Outside*
Summation Scores

Category*	N	Mean
0, most contact	4	31.75
1	10	43.30
2	23	37.96
3	12	43.75
4	15	43.87
5, least contact	12	35.67
Total	76	

* There were no Ss whose *Contact with outside* rating was 2, 2, 2, or sum 6.

In Table G-1 we can see that the two sets of data were unrelated in any meaningful direction. Insofar as the patient is not given the opportunity to practice the behavior or attain experience related to the items on the test when he is out of the hospital, this result is understandable.

From these analyses we were encouraged to relate the amount of increase in the Assessment Test scores, after the experiment, to years in the hospital. We reasoned that greater increase would be shown among the groups of patients who had been in the hospital a shorter length of time.

✑§ RESULTS AND OBSERVATIONS §✎

There were two independent variables in the study. The first of these was the method of instruction. We predicted that there would be a significant increase in the scores of those patients who received instruction for twenty sessions through the discussion method followed by the alternate method, and least improvement in the scores of those who received instruction through the demonstration method only. The same result would be reflected in the follow-up scores after six weeks, attesting to the superiority of the discussion method for chronic mental patients.

The second independent variable was time. There was reason to believe that if the same information was given during a briefer period, the demonstration method would prove most beneficial because there would not be enough time, in the discussion method, to probe the material in any depth.

We also predicted a significant increase in the scores of those patients who received instruction for ten sessions through the demonstration method followed by the alternate method, and least improvement in the scores of those patients who had the discussion method only. The same result would be reflected among the methods in the data for the follow-up of these patients.

The various means of the series of initial testing, retests, and follow-up scores for the groups according to time and methods appear in Table G-2.

TABLE G-2

Mean Assessment Test Scores for Groups Before and
After Instruction and Six Weeks Follow-up

Groups	N	Be-fore	After	Follow-up	t^a	t^b
Demonstration (20)	6	26.67	35.17	34.33	3.905**	5.463***
Demonstration (20)	7	27.43	39.14	38.57	3.839***	2.863*
Demonstration (10)	5	33.20	39.60	44.20	2.483	3.808**
Discussion (20)	7	25.71	37.71	36.71	5.500***	2.830*
Discussion (20)	7	29.43	35.43	38.71	3.291**	3.502**
Discussion (10)	5	33.40	41.00	41.00	3.453**	2.418
Alternate (20)	6	28.17	38.50	33.67	3.100*	3.642**
Alternate (20)	6	25.33	33.33	32.17	6.420***	4.324***
Alternate (10)	5	33.80	37.20	40.00	2.806*	4.360**
Control (20)	6	28.50	32.83	33.50	3.533**	5.578***
Control (10)	6	33.00	34.67	36.83	3.003*	2.600*
Total	66					

* $p < .05$
** $p < .02$
*** $p < .01$
[a] Test between pre-test and post-testing.
[b] Test between post-testing and follow-up.

A close inspection of these data means reveals that, for the longer period of instruction, all groups, except one discussion group, scored lower after six weeks than they did on the day following the termination of the instruction, when the retest was administered. This drop was significant for all groups (excluding controls, t = 7.73, 38 df, p < .001). One other exception to this general drop in scores was the control groups, which, in both lengths of time (five and ten weeks of instruction) continued to show a significant rise in scores. This result is interpreted as showing the effect that living in the rehabilitation hospital had upon the knowledge of the topics tested. Another group of patients matched with these upon the variables of WAIS scores and length of hospitalization failed to show a rise in scores on the Assessment Test after the same periods (N = 14, seven for each time period). The means of the control groups of patients were higher than four of the nine experimental groups. A more realistic appraisal is made when one compares these data between the two time periods. For the longer period, the control mean was above that of only one group (an alternate method group), and for the shorter period of time, the control group mean was the lowest. Instruction, therefore, served to increase the follow-up scores regardless of the method used.

The least effective methods were the short-term discussion method and demonstration method. There was generally less change among the five-week groups altogether.

For the longer, ten-week, period it appears from the data means that the discussion method was superior with follow-up testing; the two other methods showed extreme variation between the two groups within the methods. The alternate method was not as beneficial in increasing scores as the demonstration method, but there was no concise trend in the means.

We analyzed the discrepancy between the means for the shorter instruction period. The discussion method is initially superior but is "overtaken" upon follow-up by the demonstration method, as predicted. The data of the alternate method again show a lower rate of increase between the levels of the "pure" methods and the control group.

The results of the analyses of the data appear in Table G-3. The groups means, and therefore the method and control means, fail to differ due to the extreme variance between the subjects in the same group. The means between testings differ significantly, and we conclude that training increases scores but no method is superior. The discussion method failed to achieve the predicted result for the twenty-session groups. There was a definite trend, however, in the discussion method groups, which suggests that a continuation of the experimental teaching sessions would have given these groups a very similar level of mean scores, whereas a great discrepancy was found between the groups in the other methods.

The intrasubject and intramethod variations suggest that there are subject variables more important than method.

TABLE G-3

Analysis of Variance of Performance Scores of Seven Groups of Subjects Taught Under Different Methods and a Control With Pre-, Post-, and Follow-up Tests

Source of Variation	Ss	df	MS	F
Between Groups:	208.91	6	34.82	n.s.
Between Ss in Same Group:	7868.53	38	207.07	
Total Between Ss:	8077.44	44		
Between Testings:	2111.00	2	1055.50	33.08*
Interaction: Testings X Groups	385.36	12	32.11	1.01
Interaction: Ss X Testings	2425.20	76	31.91	
Total Within Ss:	4921.56	90		
Total:	12999.00	134		

* $p < .001$

The means at the end of the ten-session instruction period showed the following: demonstration method, 39.60; discussion method, 41.00; alternate method, 37.20; control, 34.67; and there was a reversal between the first two methods upon follow-up after six weeks, as shown in Table G-2. Table G-4 shows the results of the analysis of these data, and they reveal a similar finding to that of the longer instruction period analysis.

The differences between pre-instruction, post-instruction, and follow-up were significant, and the methods were not, due to

TABLE G-4

Analysis of Variance of Performance Scores of Four Groups
Taught Under Different Methods and a Control with Pre-, Post-,
and Follow-up Tests (10 Sessions)

Source of Variation	Ss	df	MS	F
Between Methods:	174.08	3	58.03	n.s.
Between Ss in				
Same Group:	1742.86	17	102.52	
Total Between Ss:	1916.94	20		
Between Testings:	532.01	2	266.00	21.25*
Interaction:				
Testings X Methods	106.45	6	17.74	1.42
Interaction:				
Ss X Testings	425.56	34	12.52	
Total Within Ss:	977.38	42		
Total:	2894.32	62		

* p < .01

the size of the error term, or the variation between subjects in the same group. The variation between subjects was not significant when the groups were formed (see Table G-2).

What factors contributed to the differential increase in scores irrespective of types of instruction? In order to investigate this problem, we took as our measure the change scores between the pre-instruction and post-instruction assessments for each subject and related these indices with some factors that we discussed earlier.

From what we knew about the relationship between performance on the Assessment Test and length of hospitalization, it was most likely that this variable would determine the learning ability of the subjects on the test. Our anticipated relationship was not shown ($r_s = -.07$, $t = .306$, 53 df). Learning, however, was correlated with IQ to a significant extent ($r_s = .92$, $t = 16.94$, 53 df, $p < .001$).

Yet another factor could have contributed to the individual differences in assessment test score increases. This factor was specifically defined in terms of overt behavior and qualitative differences between the patients.

Throughout the patients' stay in the rehabilitation hospital, a routine rating schedule is maintained on each patient by the nurses. This is called the Behavior Report (Wing, 1960) and is divided into two parts: socially embarrassing acts (the numerical right-hand score), such as raucous talking in a public place or in the hospital dining room, and social withdrawal (the numerical left-hand score), such as occasional muteness. Scores are assigned to these indices so that the patient exhibiting neither of these tendencies receives a rating of 0:0. Summing the ratings given the patients in the groups at the time they were placed in the instruction courses yielded a range from 0 to 12. These ratings were correlated with the change scores and found to be significant ($r_s = .905$, $t = 15.14$, 53 df, $p < .001$).

It was obvious that without further sessions and reinforcement from the instructors many patients would fail to retain what they had learned. Was this loss of retention due to any of the factors investigated above? We took as the index the difference between post-instruction score and follow-up score and related these differences to the measures.

Almost half (48 per cent) of the subjects' scores decreased when the assessment test was administered a third time. The relationship between length of hospitalization and the follow-up scores was significant ($r_s = .91$, $t = 15.84$, 53 df, $p < .001$) indicating that a patient who had been hospitalized a reasonably shorter period of time exhibited greater recall than a patient who had been hospitalized for a longer time. The average years in the hospital for this group was 16.2; a score increase was made by those patients who had no longer than fifteen years in the hospital. These patients' length of hospitalization was not related to their ability to learn in the program, but only to recall *after* learning.

A reverse result was obtained when IQ scores were related to the follow-up change scores showing that retention of the material and IQ were not associated ($r_s = .02$, $t = .1456$, 53 df).

There was another reversal when the Behavior Report scores were considered along with retention. There was no obtained relationship between this index and follow-up change ($r_s = .01$, $t = .0438$, 53 df), whereas we had found the scores associated with improved performance immediately after a course of instruction.

Learning while in the groups was related to higher intelligence and "better" Behavior Report scores, or less social withdrawal and overt symptoms. Retention of this material was related to a shorter stay in the parent hospital, but not related to the other two factors. It would appear, therefore, that in the short interval, patients should be screened for basic intelligence and manifestation of illness for group membership. If one wishes the patient to be able to repeat his performance at a later date, length of hospitalization is an important consideration.

The question remains concerning the interrelationship between hospitalization longevity, intelligence, and Behavior Report. In view of the results reported thus far, and the magnitude of the correlations that were found, interrelationships between the indices would be unlikely. Further analyses showed that these variables were related, but in an unexpected way: higher IQ was associated with longer hospitalization ($r_s = .40$, $t = 3.148$, 53 df, $p < .01$); higher IQ was also associated with a "better" Behavior Report ($r_s = .32$, $t = 2.436$, 53 df, $p < .02$); but longer hospitalization was associated with a "poorer" Behavior Report ($r_s = .24$, $t = 1.78$, 53 df, $p < .05$).

These contradictions appear to lie in the higher correlations obtained between intelligence and the other two indices. Length of hospitalization was, however, the most crucial variable. Careful inspection of the data indicated that, among the more intelligent patients, there were longer periods of time spent in the hospital and "better" Behavior Reports, whereas the patients with lower intelligence and the same length of time in the hospital had "poorer" Behavior Reports. Among the more intelligent of the patients with higher IQ's and "better" reports, more learning occurred, but with a loss in retention. Those with a shorter period of time in the hospital, regardless of their intelligence, were able to retain and reproduce the material. The erosive effect of a long hospitalization did not interfere with learning ability, but did affect retention. These are only suggestive results, and no causal relationship can be inferred.

The difficulty of establishing rapport with a person in a poor mental condition probably accounts for the positive association between IQ and Behavior Report. IQ and the Report are thus redundant for predicting an increase in learning—either will serve. They are equally redundant for predicting retention—neither will serve. In order for patients to reap the greatest benefit from such a program, it appears that they should be selected on two criteria, and that length of hospitalization should be one of them.

The individual patterning of the three scores took the form of increase following the training experience, and decreased or remained the same upon follow-up in 54 per cent of the cases. There was a steady increase in all assessments in 38 per cent of the cases. The remaining patterns (8 per cent) showed an erratic drop after group sessions and a rise with follow-up. No cases showed a steady downward series of scores with repeated testing.

Most of the cases that showed decrease in scores were evenly distributed between the discussion and alternate groups. Absences did not contribute to this phenomenon. There were thirty days of absences in the demonstration method groups, forty-four days of absences in the discussion method groups, and forty-five in the alternate groups.

These phenomena were not related to any extent to a particular part of the hospital from which the patients originated. The experimental subjects were selected on the basis of their Assessment Test scores and the groups were consequently composed of patients from the four workshops in disproportionate numbers: Twenty-seven were from the chronic unit, eight from the intake unit, ten from the middle unit, and eight from the discharge unit. The mean increases of the patients between units were: Chronic, 9.29; intake, 12.00; middle, 4.55; discharge, 9.125. Analysis of these data was not significant ($F = 1.613$, 3 and 50 df, $p < .05$), although the sub-sample from the middle unit did not fare so well in the program. There were no greater number of class absences among subjects from this unit than among subjects from the others, so the number of absences did not contribute to the result.

Bibliography

ALLPORT, G. W. *Pattern and Growth in Personality.* New York: Holt, 1961.

ALTSCHUL, A. T. "Trends in psychiatric nursing." In H. Freeman and J. Farndale (Eds.), *Trends in the Mental Health Services.* London: Pergamon, 1963.

AMBRE, A. "Where the action is." *Occupational Outlook Quarterly.* 1966, *10,* 32.

ARIETI, S. "Volition and value: a study based on catatonic schizophrenia." *Comprehensive Psychiatry,* 1961, *2,* 74–82.

BANDURA, A., ROSS, D., and ROSS, S. A. "A comparative test of the status envy, social power, and secondary reinforcement theories of identificatory learning." *Journal of Abnormal and Social Psychology,* 1963, *67,* 527–534.

BARTON, R. *Institutional Neurosis.* Bristol: John Wright, 1959.

BELKNAP, J. *Human Problems of a State Mental Hospital.* New York: McGraw-Hill, 1956.

BENNE, K. D. and BENNIS, W. "Role confusion and conflict in nursing: the role of the professional nurse." *American Journal of Nursing,* 1959, *59,* 196–198.

BENNETT, C. H. and WING, J. D. "Sheltered workshops for the psychiatrically handicapped." In H. Freeman and J. Farndale (Eds.), *Trends in the Mental Health Services.* London: Pergamon, 1963.

BORDIN, E. S. "Curiosity, compassion and doubt: the dilemma of the psychologist." *American Psychologist,* 1966, *21,* 116–121.

BOROW, H. (Ed.) *Man in a World at Work.* Boston: Houghton Mifflin, 1964.

BROWN, E. L. *Newer Dimensions of Patient Care.* New York: Russell Sage Foundation, 1961.

BRUNER, J. S., OLVER, R. R., and GREENFIELD, P. M. *Studies in Cognitive Growth: A Collaboration at the Center for Cognitive Studies.* New York: Wiley, 1966.

CAMPBELL, D. T., MILLER, N., LUBETSKY, J., and O'CONNELL, W. J. "Varieties of projection in trait attribution." *Psychological Monographs,* 1964, *78.*

CHEADLE, A. J., CUSHING, D., DREW, C. D. A., and MORGAN, R. "The measurement of the work performance of psychiatric patients." *British Journal of Psychiatry,* 1967, *113,* 841–846.

COLARELLI, N. J. and SIEGEL, S. M. *Ward H: An Adventure in Innovation.* Princeton: Van Nostrand, 1966.

CORWIN, R. G. and TAVES, M. J. "Nursing and other health professions." In H. E. Freeman, S. Levine and L. G. Reeder (Eds.), *Handbook of Medical Sociology*. Englewood Cliffs, N. J.: Prentice-Hall, 1963.

COWDEN, R. C. "Problem-solving in schizophrenics as a function of motivation." *Psychological Report,* 1962, *10,* 627–633.

COZENS, W. R. "The relationship between social withdrawal and intellectual test performance in the hospitalized, chronic schizophrenic." American Psychological Association convention paper, 1964.

CRUMPTON, E. "Persistence of maladaptive responses in schizophrenia." *Journal of Abnormal Psychology,* 1963, *66,* 615–618.

CUMMING, J. and CUMMING, E. *Ego and Milieu: Theory and Practice of Environmental Therapy.* New York: Atherton, 1962.

DIGGORY, J. C. and LOEB, A. "Motivation of chronic schizophrenics by information about their abilities in a group situation." *Journal of Abnormal and Social Psychology,* 1962, *65,* 48–52.

DRAGUNS, J. C. "Responses to cognitive and perceptual ambiguity in chronic and acute schizophrenics." *Journal of Abnormal and Social Psychology,* 1963, *66,* 24–30.

EARL, C. J. C. *Subnormal Personalities: Their Clinical Investigation and Assessment* (with additional material by H. C. Gunzburg). Baltimore: Williams and Wilkins, 1961.

EDELSON, M. *Ego Psychology, Group Dynamics, and the Therapeutic Community.* New York: Grune and Stratton, 1965.

EYSENCK, H. J. (Ed.) *Handbook of Abnormal Psychology: An Experimental Approach.* New York: Basic Books, 1961.

FAGAN, J. and GUTHRIE, G. M. "Perception of self and normality in schizophrenics." *Journal of Clinical Psychology,* 1959, *15,* 203–207.

FAIRWEATHER, G. W. (Ed.) *Social Psychology in Treating Mental Illness.* New York: Wiley, 1964.

FARIS, R. E. L. and DUNHAM, H. W. *Mental Disorders in Urban Areas.* Chicago: University of Chicago Press, 1939.

FESTINGER, L. *A Theory of Cognitive Dissonance.* Evanston, Ill.: Row, Peterson, 1957.

FISHMAN, L. (Ed.) *Poverty Amid Affluence.* New Haven: Yale University Press, 1966.

FRANKE, W. H. "The long-term unemployed." In J. M. Becker (Ed.),

In Aid of the Unemployed. Baltimore: Johns Hopkins Press, 1965.

FREEMAN, H. E. and SIMMONS, O. G. *The Mental Patient Comes Home*. New York: Wiley, 1963.

FREEMAN, R. A. "Public works and work relief." In J. M. Becker (Ed.), *In Aid of the Unemployed*. Baltimore: John Hopkins Press, 1965.

FROMM, E. *Man for Himself: An Inquiry into the Psychology of Ethics*. New York: Rinehart, 1947.

GIBBONS, D. C. *Changing the Lawbreaker: The Treatment of Delinquents and Criminals*. Englewood Cliffs, N. J.: Prentice-Hall, 1965.

GILBERT, D. C. and LEVINSON, D. J. " 'Custodialism' and 'humanism' in mental hospital structure and in staff ideology." In M. Greenblatt, D. J. Levinson and R. H. Williams (Eds.), *The Patient and the Mental Hospital*. New York: Free Press, 1957.

GOFFMAN, E. *Asylums*. Chicago: Aldine, 1962.

GOLDMAN, A. B. "Differential effects of social reward and punishment on dependent and dependency-anxious schizophrenics." *Journal of Abnormal Psychology*, 1965, *70*, 412–418.

GOODMAN, P. *People or Personnel: Decentralizing and the Mixed System*. New York: Random House, 1965.

GORDON, M. S. (Ed.) *Poverty in America*. San Francisco: Chandler, 1966.

GOUGH, H. *Manual for the California Psychological Inventory*. Palo Alto, Calif.: Consulting Psychologists Press, 1960.

GUNZBURG, H. C. *Social Rehabilitation of the Subnormal*. Baltimore: Williams and Wilkins, 1960.

HAAS, W. A. "Motivation in schizophrenic patients." *Psychological Report*, 1963, *12*, 799–802.

HAAS, H. I. and MAEHR, M. L. "Two experiments on the concept of self and the reaction of others." *Journal of Personality and Social Psychology*, 1965, *1*, 100–105.

HAIGH, G. "Fieldtraining in human relations for the Peace Corps." *Journal of Social Psychology*, 1966, *68*, 3–13.

HAMILTON, V. "IQ changes in chronic schizophrenia." *British Journal of Psychiatry*, 1963, *190*, 642–648.

HARRINGTON, M. *The Other America: Poverty in the United States*. New York: Macmillan, 1964.

HAYWOOD, E. C. and MOELIS, J. "Effect of symptom change on intellectual function in schizophrenia." *Journal of Abnormal and Social Psychology*, 1963, *67*, 76–78.

HENRY, J. "Types of institutional structure." *Psychiatry,* 1957, *20,* 47–60.

———. *Culture Against Man.* New York: Random House, 1963.

HERZBERG, F., MAUSNER, B., and SYNDERMAN, B. B. *The Motivation to Work.* New York: Wiley, 1962.

HILLSON, J. S. and WORCHEL, P. "Self-concept and defensive behavior in the maladjusted." *Journal of Consulting Psychology,* 1957, *21,* 83–88.

HINKLE, L. E. and WOLFF, H. G. "Health and social environment: experimental investigations." In A. C. Leighton, J. A. Clausen and R. N. Wilson (Eds.), *Explorations in Social Psychiatry.* New York: Basic Books, 1957.

HOLLINGSHEAD, A. B. *Two-factor Index of Social Position.* Mimeographed publication, Department of Sociology, Yale University, 1957.

——— and REDLICH, F. C. *Social Class and Mental Illness: A Community Study.* New York: Wiley, 1958.

HOOVER, K. K. "An operational analysis of the philosophy, methods, and results of the Downey Motivation Unit." Research plan, personal communication, 1962.

JOHNSON, R. C., WEISS, R. L., and ZELKART, S. "Similarities and differences between normal and psychotic subjects in responses to verbal stimuli." *Journal of Abnormal and Social Psychology,* 1964, *68,* 221–226.

JONES, M. *The Therapeutic Community.* New York: Basic Books, 1953.

KAGAN, J. "The concept of identification." *Psychological Review,* 1958, *65,* 296–305.

KAHN, R. L., WOLFE, D. M., QUINN, R. P., SNOEK, J. D., and ROSENTHAL, R. A. *Organizational Stress: Studies in Role Conflict and Ambiguity.* New York: Wiley, 1964.

KAMANO, D. K. "Self-satisfaction and psychological adjustment in schizophrenics." *Journal of Consulting Psychology,* 1961, *25,* 492–496.

KANDEL, D. B. and WILLIAMS, R. H. *Psychiatric Rehabilitation: Some Problems of Research.* New York: Atherton, 1964.

KELLY, F. C. and VELDMAN, D. J. "Delinquency and school drop-out behavior as a function of impulsivity and nondominant values." *Journal of Abnormal and Social Psychology,* 1964, *69,* 190–194.

KOLB, D. "Achievement motivation training for under-achieving high school boys." *Journal of Personality and Social Psychology,* 1965, *2,* 783–792.

KORNHAUSER, A. *Mental Health of the Industrial Worker: A Detroit Study*. New York: Wiley, 1965.

LA FAVE, H. G., LAWBY, L. R., BURKE, J. L., COHEN, M. E., HARRINGTON, L., and LEE, H. "Intensive rehabilitation for chronic patients." *Mental Hospitals*, 1965, *16*, 279–281.

LANDY, D. and RAULET, H. "The hospital work program." In M. Greenblatt and A. B. Simon (Eds.), *Rehabilitation of the Mentally Ill*. Washington, D. C.: American Association for the Advancement of Science, 1959, *58*, 71–87.

LEIGHTON, A. C., HARDING, J. S., MACKLIN, B. B., MacMILLAN, A. M., and LEIGHTON, A. H. *The Character of Danger*. New York: Basic Books, 1963.

LERNER, M. *America as a Civilization*. New York: Simon and Schuster, 1957.

LEVINSON, D. J. and GALLAGHER, E. B. *Patienthood in the Mental Hospital: An Analysis of Role, Personality, and Social Structure*. Boston: Houghton Mifflin, 1964.

LEWIS, M. "Psychological effect of effort." *Psychological Bulletin*, 1965, *64*, 183–189.

LIBO, L. "Multiple functions for psychologists in community consultation." *American Psychologist*, 1966, *21*, 530–534.

LIPSITT, D. R. "Institutional dependency: a rehabilitation problem." In M. Greenblatt, D. J. Levinson and G. L. Klerman (Eds.), *Mental Patients in Transition: Steps in Hospital-Community Rehabilitation*. Springfield, Ill.: Thomas, 1961.

LOWENTHAL, M. F., BERKMAN, P. L., and associates. *Aging and Mental Disorder in San Francisco*. San Francisco: Jossey-Bass, 1967.

MCCLELLAND, D. C., ATKINSON, J. W., CLARK, R. A., and LOWELL, E. L. *The Achievement Motive*. New York: Appleton-Century, 1953.

MACDONALD, W. S. and SHEEHAN, J. G. "Responses of schizophrenics to different incentives." *Psychological Report*, 1962, *11*, 211–217.

MCREYNOLDS, R. "Reactions to novel and familiar stimuli as a function of schizophrenic withdrawal." *Perceptual and Motor Skills*, 1963, *16*, 847–850.

MANASSE, G. "Self-regard as a function of environmental demands in chronic schizophrenics." *Journal of Abnormal Psychology*, 1965, *70*, 210–213.

MANTON, N. S. "When a hospital goes into business." *British Hospital and Social Service Journal*, 1964, *74*, 3879.

MASON, A. S. "The hospital service clinic—a work modality for the geriatric mental patient." *Journal of American Geriatric Society,* 1965, *13,* 545–549.

———, CUNNINGHAM, M. K., and TARPY, E. K. "The quarter-way house —a transitional program for chronically ill geriatric mental patients." *Journal of American Geriatric Society,* 1963, *11,* 574–579.

MEAD, G. H. *Mind, Self, and Society.* Chicago: University of Chicago Press, 1934.

MEISSNER, H. H. (Ed.) *Poverty in the Affluent Society.* New York: Harper and Row, 1966.

MILLER, H. P. (Ed.) *Poverty: American Style.* Belmont, Calif.: Wadsworth, 1966.

MORGAN, R. "The personal orientation of long-stay psychiatric patients." *British Journal of Psychiatry,* 1967, *113,* 847–885.

——— and CUSHING, D. "The personal possessions of long-stay patients in mental hospitals." *Social Psychiatry,* 1966, *1,* 151–157.

———, CUSHING, D., and MANTON, N. S. "A regional psychiatric rehabilitation hospital." *British Journal of Psychiatry,* 1965, *11,* 955–963.

MYERS, J. K. and ROBERTS, B. H. *Family and Class Dynamics in Mental Illness.* New York: Wiley, 1959.

NEWCOMB, T. M. *Social Psychology.* New York: Dryden, 1950.

Occupational Outlook Quarterly, 1966, *10,* 32. "Who are the unemployed?"

OLSON, G. W. "Failure and the subsequent performance of schizophrenics." *Journal of Abnormal and Social Psychology,* 1958, *57,* 310–314.

PARSONS, T. "Definitions of health and illness in the light of American values and social structure." In E. G. Jaco (Ed.), *Patients, Physicians, and Illness.* New York: Free Press, 1958.

PHILLIPS, J. P. N. "The response of chronic schizophrenics to different frequencies of monetary reward: a pilot study." *British Journal of Social and Clinical Psychology,* 1965, *4,* 116.

President's Committee on Youth Employment. *The Challenge of Jobless Youth,* April, 1963.

QUERY, J. M. "Premorbid adjustment and family structure: a comparison of selected rural and urban schizophrenic men." *Journal of Nervous and Mental Disease,* 1961, *133,* 333–338.

——— and QUERY, W. T. "Prognosis and progress: a five-year study of forty-eight schizophrenic men." *Journal of Consulting Psychology,* 1964, *28,* 501–505.

QUERY, W. T., MOORE, K. B., and LERNER, J. J. "Social factors and chronic schizophrenia: the effect on performance and group cohesiveness." *Psychiatric Quarterly,* 1966, *40,* 504–514.

RAPOPORT, R. N. *Community as Doctor: New Perspectives on a Therapeutic Community.* London: Tavistock, 1960.

REZNIKOFF, M., BRADY, J. P., ZELLER, W. W., and TOOMEY, L. C. "Attitudinal change in hospitalized psychiatric patients." *Journal of Clinical and Experimental Psychopathology,* 1960, *21,* 309–314.

RIESSMAN, F., COHEN, J., and PEARL, A. (Eds.) *The Mental Health of the Poor: New Treatment Approaches for Low Income People.* New York: Free Press, 1966.

ROBERTS, B. H. and MYERS, J. K. *Family and Class Dynamics in Mental Illness.* New York: Wiley, 1959.

ROE, A. *The Psychology of Occupations.* New York: Wiley, 1956.

ROMMERVEIT, R. *Social Norms and Roles: Explorations in the Psychology of Enduring Social Pressures.* Oslo: Academisch forlag, 1955.

SARBIN, T. R. "Role theory." In G. Lindzey (Ed.), *Handbook of Social Psychology,* I, *Theory and Method.* Cambridge: Addison-Wesley, 1954.

SCHER, J. M. "The concept of self in schizophrenia." *Journal of Existential Psychiatry,* 1960, *1,* 64–88.

SCHOOLER, C. "Affiliation among schizophrenics: Preferred characteristics of the other." *Journal of Nervous and Mental Disease,* 1963, 137, 438–446.

SCHWARTZ, C. H. "Problems for psychiatric nurses in playing a new role on a mental hospital ward." In M. Greenblatt, D. J. Levinson and R. H. Williams (Eds.), *The Patient and the Mental Hospital.* New York: Free press, 1957.

SEARS, R. R. "Dependency motivation." *Nebraska Symposium on Motivation,* Lincoln: University of Nebraska Press, 1963.

SHARAF, M. R. and LEVINSON, D. J. "Patterns of ideology and role definition among psychiatric patients." In M. Greenblatt, D. J. Levinson and R. H. Williams (Eds.), *The Patient and the Mental Hospital.* New York: Free Press, 1957.

SHERIF, M. and CANTRIL, H. *The Psychology of Ego-involvements.* New York: Wiley, 1947.

SIEGEL, S. *Nonparametric Statistics for the Behavioral Sciences.* New York: McGraw-Hill, 1956.

SIDLE, A., ACKER, M., and MCREYNOLDS, P. " 'Stimulus-seeking' behavior in schizophrenics and non-schizophrenics." *Perceptual and Motor Skills*, 1963, *17*, 811–816.

SIMMONS, O. G. *Work and Mental Illness: Eight Case Studies*. New York: Wiley, 1965.

SINGER, E. *Key Concepts in Psychotherapy*. New York: Random House, 1965.

SKAETH, A. "Charge nurse in a rehabilitation unit." *Nursing Times*, 1964, *60*, 1957.

SKEELS, H. M. and DYE, H. B. "A study of the effects of differential stimulation on mentally retarded children." *Proceedings of the American Association of Mental Deficiency*, 1939, *44*, 114–136.

SOMMER, R. and OSMOND, H. "The schizophrenic no-society." In J. K. Skipper and R. C. Leonard (Eds.), *Social Interaction and Patient Care*. Philadelphia: Lippincott, 1965, 306–322.

STANTON, A. H. and SCHWARTZ, M. S. *The Mental Hospital*. New York: Basic Books, 1954.

STEPHENSON, W. *The Study of Behavior: Q-Technique and Its Methodology*. Chicago: University of Chicago Press, 1953.

STIEPER, D. R. and WIENER, D. N. *The Dimensions of Psychotherapy: An Experimental and Clinical Approach*. Chicago: Aldine, 1965.

SUFRIN, S. C. and BUCK, M. A. *What Price Progress? A Study in Chronic Unemployment*. Chicago: Rand McNally, 1963.

SULLIVAN, H. S. *The Interpersonal Theory of Psychiatry*. New York: Norton, 1953.

TALBOT, E., MILLER, S. C., and WHITE, R. B. "Some aspects of self-conceptions and role demands in a therapeutic community." *Journal of Abnormal and Social Psychology*, 1961, *63*, 338–345.

TOWER: *Testing, Orientation, and Work Evaluation in Rehabilitation*. New York: Institute for the Crippled and Disabled, 1959.

Treatment Team. "Attitude therapy and the team approach." *Mental Hospitals*, November, 1965.

VROOM, V. H. *Work and Motivation*. New York: Wiley, 1964.

WALKER, H. M. and LEV, J. *Statistical Inference*. New York: Holt, 1953.

WHITE, R. W. "Sense of interpersonal competence: two case studies and some reflection on origins." In R. W. White (Ed.), *The Study of Lives: Essays on Personality in Honor of Henry A. Murray*. New York: Atherton, 1966.

——. "Motivation reconsidered: the concept of competence." *Psychological Review*, 1959, *67*, 297–333.

WHITING, J. W. M. and CHILD, I. L. *Child Training and Personality.* New Haven: Yale University Press, 1953.

WHITMAN, J. R. and DUFFEY, R. F. "The relationship between type of therapy received and a patient's perception of his illness." *Journal of Nervous and Mental Disease,* 1961, *4,* 288–292.

WILL, R. E. and VATTER, H. G. (Eds.) *Poverty in Affluence: The Social, Political, and Economic Dimensions of Poverty in the United States.* Chicago: Science Research Associates, 1964.

WING, J. K. "The measurement of behavior in chronic schizophrenia." *Acta Psychiatrica and Neurologica Scandinavia,* 1960, *35,* 245.

———. "A simple and reliable subclassification of chronic schizophrenia." *Journal of Mental Science,* 1961, *107,* 862.

WOLFBEIN, S. L. *Employment and Unemployment in the United States.* Chicago: Science Research Associates, 1964.

WOOD, M. M. *Paths of Loneliness: The Individual Isolated in Western Society.* New York: Columbia University Press, 1953.

WYATT, S. *Incentives in Repetitive Work: A Practical Experiment in a Factory.* Health Research Board, *69,* London, H.M.S.O., 1934.

ZAWADZKI, B. and LAZARSFELD, P. F. "The psychological consequences of unemployment." *Journal of Social Psychology,* 1935, 224–251.

ZEIGARNIK, B. "The memory of completed and uncompleted actions." *Psychologie Forschung,* 1927, *9,* 1–85.

Index

261

41570

DATE DUE